REVISE EDEXCEL
FUNCTIONAL SKILLS LEVEL 1

English

New College
New College Drive
Swindon
SN3 1AH
www.newcollege.ac.uk
01793 611470

REVISION WORKBOOK

Series Consultant: Harry Smith

Author: Julie Hughes

To revise all the topics covered in this book, check out:

Revise Functional Skills Level 1
English Revision Guide   978 1 292 14580 8

THE REVISE SERIES
For the full range of Pearson revision titles, visit:
www.pearsonschools.co.uk/revise

Contents

A small bit of small print

Edexcel publishes Sample Assessment Material and the Specification on its website. This is the official content and this book should be used in conjunction with it. The questions in this book have been written to help you practise what you have learned in your revision. Remember: the real test questions may not look like this.

Your reading and writing tests

Preparing for your reading and writing tests will help you to do well in your Functional Skills qualification.

> Use this workbook to prepare for your tests. Use the contents page to go to topics that you feel unsure about, or work through each topic from start to finish.

1   How long will your reading test last?
    Answer the question by placing a cross in one of the boxes below.

    ☐ **A** 13 minutes

    ☐ **B** 2 hours

    ☐ **C** 45 minutes

    ☐ **D** 20 minutes

2   How many texts will you need to read in your reading test?

    ....

3   How many tasks will you need to complete in your writing test?
    Circle the answer you think is correct.

    1   2   3   4

> **GUIDED**

4   Complete the table by filling in the missing word in the first column and by writing the number of minutes you should spend on each writing task.

Planning Task 1	5 minutes
Writing and checking **Task 1**	....
Planning Task 2	....
Writing and .... **Task 2**	....

5   List **two** things you should do during the planning stage.

    ....

    ....

    ....

    ....

Reading test skills

> **GUIDED**   **1**   What will the reading test texts have in common?

The texts will be about the same theme or ....

2   Which of the following text types might be used for your reading test?
Circle all the answers you think are correct.

letter	advert	book	ticket	newspaper article

> **GUIDED**   **3**   Complete the following explanations of the skills you will need in your reading test by filling in the gaps. Use the words at the bottom of each section.

Identify the main points and ideas and explain how they are presented in a variety of texts

Text titles often make the main idea of a text clear. Writers use different ways to present texts

to help .... find information easily. For example, a writer might use headings, sub-

headings and ....

clear	bold fonts	readers	titles

(clear and titles crossed out)

Read and understand texts in detail

Writers .... their main ideas by adding ....

detail	develop

Use the information you find in texts

Readers use the information in texts in lots of .... ways. For example, texts

can be used to .... people to do something, or to ....

people about how to do something.

inform	persuade	different

Identify how to respond to a text

Texts often ask for some sort of .... from readers. For example, a text might

ask readers to sign up for further ...., or it might ask readers to write a letter

of ....

reply	action	information

Multiple choice questions

You need to know how to answer multiple choice questions in your reading test.

1   What should you do if you change your mind about the answer, but have already put a cross in one of the boxes?

....

2   Look at this test-style multiple choice question and a student's answer.

> The **main** purpose of the leaflet is:
> ☒ **A**   to tell the reader how good a top chef's food can be
> ☒ **B**   to persuade the reader to book a cookery cruise
> ☐ **C**   to give the reader advice about cruises
> ☐ **D**   to encourage the reader to take up cookery   **(1 mark)**

What is wrong with the student's answer?

....

3   Look at this test-style question.

> Identify .... features from the list below that show that Text B is a letter.
> ☐ **A**   address
> ☐ **B**   date
> ☐ **C**   use of 'Dear'
> ☐ **D**   headings
> ☐ **E**   punctuation   **(2 marks)**

How many features should you identify to get the full marks for this question?

Fill in the gap in the question.

GUIDED **4**   Which **three** of the following statements are helpful pieces of advice about multiple choice questions?

☐ **A**   Make sure you read the question carefully.

☐ **B**   Look at how many marks are available. This will tell you how many answers are needed.

☒ **C**   Put a line through any mistakes.

☐ **D**   Always give only one answer per question.

Short response questions

You need to know how to answer short response questions in your reading test.

1   Which **one** of the following statements about short response questions is true?

☐ **A**   You do not need to write your answer in full sentences.

☐ **B**   You must always write your answers in full sentences.

☐ **C**   The information needed will always be together in one part of the text.

☐ **D**   You should make sure you fill the whole of the dotted line with your answer.

2   Choose **two** of the incorrect statements in question 1 above. Explain why each is incorrect.

☐ ....

....

☐ ....

....

Look at this student's answer to this test-style question, then answer questions 3 and 4 below.

Your friend is thinking about applying for a foundation plumbing course at Estrick College, but is worried that he will not get enough support. Using Text C, give **two** ways in which the college supports students.

You do **not** need to write in sentences.

1   If students are short of money they can get some help with the costs of

transport to get to college.

2   They can also get help with buying tools.

(2 marks)

3   Give **two** reasons why this is not the best way to answer a short response question.

....

....

....

....

4   Why are certain words in bold in the question?

....

Had a go ☐   **Nearly there** ☐   **Nailed it!** ☐

Reading the question

You should read all the questions in the reading test carefully to make sure you understand exactly what you are being asked to do.

Read the test-style question below. You don't need to answer it. Instead, think about what it is asking you to do, then answer questions 1 and 2 below.

The **main** purpose of the letter is to:

☐ **A**   inform the reader about online booking systems.

☐ **B**   persuade the reader to use a diary for appointments.

☐ **C**   tell the reader how to increase profits.

☐ **D**   inform the reader how to get more appointments.   **(1 mark)**

GUIDED   **1**   Why is the **bold** word important in the question?

Because it tells you to look for the main purpose of the letter, not all the

different purposes it might have.

2   Why is it important to read all the answer options in a multiple choice question very carefully?

....

....

Read the test-style question below. You don't need to answer it. Instead, think about what it is asking you to do, then answer the questions that follow.

Your friend does not think that safety is important when he goes to the gym.
Using Text E, give **two** reasons why your friend should think about safety in the gym.
You do **not** need to write in sentences.

1   ....

....

2   ....

....

     (2 marks)

---

3   Underline the important words that will help you to answer it correctly.

4   Would it help if you already knew a lot about gym safety? Explain your answer.

....

....

Had a go ☐   Nearly there ☐   Nailed it! ☐

Skimming for details

You can identify the main ideas in a text by skim reading it and focusing on key parts.

Read Text G on page 80 and answer questions 1–4.

GUIDED 1 Where is the best place in this letter to look for the main idea?

   The title – this often contains the main idea of a text.

2 What do the first **two** sentences of the first paragraph tell you about the purpose of the letter?

   ....

3 What should you do before skim reading the text?

   ....

Read these test-style questions carefully. You don't need to answer them. Think about what they are asking you to do and then answer question 4.

---

1 Give **one** way to find out more information about online booking systems.

   ....

   .... **(1 mark)**

2 Using the information in Text G, identify **two** reasons why telephone booking is a problem for customers.

   ....

   .... **(2 marks)**

3 A friend of yours is interested in an online booking system, but does not think there will be any advantages for his business. Identify **two** reasons why online booking systems can benefit a business.

   ....

   .... **(2 marks)**

4 Your friend wants to make a salon appointment.
   Using the information in Text G, give **two** reasons why your friend should go to a salon that has an online booking system.

   ....

   .... **(2 marks)**

 GUIDED 4 Which paragraph in Text G would you look for the answers to the questions above? Put your answers in the table below.

Question number	1	2	3	4
Paragraph number	....	....	4	....

Underlining

1   Name **two** things you should look out for when you are underlining.

....

....

Underlining key words and phrases can help you identify important information in the reading test.
Read the test-style question and an extract from Text F below.

> Your friend wants to go on a European river cruise, but does not think he will like any of the boats. Using Text F, give **two** reasons why your friend might enjoy a European river cruise.
>
> You do **not** need to write in sentences.
>
> **1** ....
>
> **2** .... **(2 marks)**

Text F

The European River Boat Company started with one narrow boat over thirty years ago.
Now, we have 15 boats touring the rivers of Europe. We are the biggest European river cruise operator. As none of our boats takes more than 20 guests at any time, you are guaranteed personal service of the highest possible standard. All rooms on board have en-suite facilities and free wi-fi. The décor is stylish and all the rooms are spacious.

If you have a passion for food and wine, we have added some exciting cookery cruises to our programme for 2017. All courses are taught by top European chefs.

---

2   Underline the key words and phrases in the question and extract. Answer the question.

Now read this test-style question and think about what it is asking you to do.

> Using Text F, identify **two** activities **other than cookery lessons** that are available on board.
>
> **1** ....
>
> **2** .... **(2 marks)**

3   Skim read the whole of Text F on page 79. Underline any information that will help you answer the question above.

> Always read the questions carefully before you start to underline any text.

Online tools 1

If you complete the Functional Skills test online, you will need to understand how the test works.

1   Give **two** reasons why it is important to know how to use the online test **before** you start it.

....

....

....

....

2   There are some useful icons across the top of the online test screen.
Instructions for the most useful icons are printed below.
Match the instructions with the correct buttons.

> Remember that the timer does not stop when you use the 'Help' feature.

? Help	You can click this icon to find out how much time you have left in your test. The time will appear in the bottom left corner of the screen.
🕐 Time	You can click this icon if you want a demonstration of how the online test buttons work.
⚠ Quit	These buttons move you from question to question.
◀ Previous ▶ Next	Be very careful with this icon. If you click on it and then click on 'Yes', you will not be able to return to the test, even if you haven't finished!

GUIDED   3   Label buttons 1–4 in the Settings box with explanations about how they can help you in your test.

switch colours   *This changes the colour of the text to make it easier to read.*

zoom reset   ....

colour reset   ....

⬆   ....

Online tools 2

The online test has useful tools that can help you to plan your answers and your time.

GUIDED 1 The notepad tool takes you to the notepad screen. Give **two** ways in which the notepad is useful during your test.

You can use the notepad to underline key words in questions.

....

GUIDED 2 The buttons below will appear across the top of the screen during your writing test. You can use them to change the layout and look of your writing. List **three** presentation features that these buttons will help you to use. Draw an arrow to the button you are explaining.

| Arial | ∨ | ■ ∨ | 12 ∨ | B | *I* | U | ≡ | ≡ | ≡ | ≡ | ≡ |

This button can be used to make titles and headings bold.

....

....

3 How will these buttons help you if you are unsure about the answer to a question?

[✓ Flag]

....

[Ⓐ Review]

....

4 In the test, you will be reminded when you have five minutes left. Which of the following should you do during these five minutes? Put a cross in the box you think is correct.

☐ **A** Click the 'Quit' button if you are finished.

☐ **B** Use the time to check your answers.

☐ **C** Click the 'Help' button for more instructions.

☐ **D** Use the time to underline key words in the questions.

5 The online test does not auto-correct spelling mistakes.
Circle the words below that are spelled incorrectly.

| Febuary | peice | fierce | autum | happened |

6 The online test does not auto-correct capital letters. Circle the words below that should always have an initial capital letter

| i | you | jenny | liverpool | mr ronaldo |

Putting it into practice

Read the following test-style questions. You don't need to answer them. Think carefully about what they are asking you to do and answer questions 1 and 2 below.

---

1   According to Text J, identify **two** leisure activities available in Tanzania.

☐   A   visiting game reserves

☐   B   viewing wildlife

☐   C   helping in an orphanage

☐   D   swimming

☐   E   sunbathing

☐   F   playing football   **(2 marks)**

2   Your friend wants to volunteer in Tanzania, but thinks he does not need to use a specialist volunteering company. Using Text J, give **two** reasons to persuade your friend to use a specialist company to organise his trip.

You do **not** need to write in sentences.

1   ....

2   ....

                                                                                                (2 marks)

3   According to Text J, where can you find details of specialist volunteering companies?

You do **not** need to write in sentences.

....

                                                                                                (1 mark)

---

1   Now skim read Text J on page 83. As you read, underline any information in the text that would help you to answer the questions above.

2   When you have skim read the whole text, go back and read the questions again.
Is the information you have underlined relevant to the questions? Have you underlined the right amount of information for each question? If not, make a note here of things you think you could improve.

....

....

....

Understanding the main idea

You need to understand the main ideas in a text to help you to identify the type of text and its purpose.

1   What are the **main** ideas in a text? Put a cross in the box next to the answer you think is correct.

☐   **A**   The main points a writer wants a reader to understand.

☐   **B**   The main points in the first paragraph.

☐   **C**   The way a writer wants a reader to feel.

☐   **D**   The information given at the end of a text.

2   Name **one** of the first places you should look for the main idea in a text.

....

3   Look at the text extract below. Draw an arrow from each feature to an example in the text.

images   bold font   title   bullet points

HEALTH & SAFETY IN THE GYM

50% of gym injuries are caused by incorrect or careless use of equipment. Please follow these simple rules to make sure no one gets hurt while using the equipment

- Use a spotter when lifting the weights.
- Read the instructions for each piece of equipment before using.

Exercise is a good way to keep fit and healthy. Make sure you think about your health at all times when using the gym:

- Always wipe down equipment before and after use.
- Drink plenty of water when exercising.
- Warm up before exercising.

4   Use the features in the extract above to identify the type of text. Circle the answer you think is correct.

| web page   blog   poster   letter |

5   Use the features you labelled in question 3 to identify the main purpose of the text above.

....

Identifying the main idea

The first thing you should do when you read a text is identify the writer's main idea.

〉GUIDED〉 **1** Usually, the main idea of a text is clear from the title. Identify the main idea in each of the titles below and write it in your own words in the box provided.

| Report into shopping facilities in Estrick High Street | ....

| HEALTH & SAFETY IN THE GYM | *How to stay safe and get healthy in the gym*

| European River Boat Company Cookery tours | ....

〉GUIDED〉 **2** Sometimes, the main idea is not obvious from the title. Look at this title and then read the first paragraph to find the main idea.

> **Animal Magic blog**
>
> Well, I did it! Today was my first day volunteering at the shelter and I loved every minute! I had a safety training session as soon as I arrived. This taught me everything from how to enter a dog kennel and how to handle a small mammal to how to wear my gloves correctly! I then went on a tour to learn about how the shelter works.

The title suggests that the blog will be something to do with animals. The first paragraph

suggests that the **main** idea is ....

〉GUIDED〉 **3** The title of the text below suggests that the main idea is straightforward. Read the first paragraph of the text to see if it is actually a bit more complicated.

> **Online Booking Systems**
>
> Thank you for your interest in our online booking system. I understand you are not sure of the benefits of an online booking system. I hope that I can give you all the information you need to make up your mind.

The title suggests that the **main** idea is

....

The first paragraph suggests that the **main** idea is

....

Identifying types of text

You need to understand the main features of each of the types of text you could come across in the test.

1   Give **two** differences in layout between emails and letters.

....

....

⟩ GUIDED ⟩   2   Label the **main** features of the three texts below.

Text A

www.estrickchoir.co.uk   Search

| Home | Meeting dates | Who we are | Helping out | Special offers | Links to other singing sites |

THE ESTRICK TUNELESS CHOIR
Did a teacher ask you to keep quiet in music lessons at school? Do you only sing out loud when you're alone in the car?

If you answered yes to any of the above questions, then read on.
The Tuneless Choir was set up in 2010 by Bernie Godfrey as an alternative to formal choir groups. It is for people like you who avoid singing aloud in public. We welcome anybody, regardless of age, gender or ability. We now have over 60 regular members and meet twice a month in Estrick Church Hall. For the past two years we have given a Christmas Concert in the church.

Text I

🐾 **ANIMAL MAGIC BLOG**

FIRST DAY!

Posted on April 2nd

Well, I did it! Today was my first day volunteering at the shelter and I loved every minute! I had a safety training session as soon as I arrived. This taught me everything from how to enter a dog kennel and how to handle a small mammal to how to wear my gloves correctly! I then went on a tour to learn about how the shelter works. Did you know that most animals are here because they are just abandoned on the roadside? A few come in because their owners can't manage them any more. Some even come for a short time when their owners are ill or away. We look after them all and try to get them back to full health.

Leave a reply:

SIGN UP TO MY NEWLETTERS!

Archive:
• March
• February
• January
• December
• November

Text J

Heading

WANT TO GIVE SOMETHING BACK? TRY VOLUNTEERING!
By Nora Galetti

If you just fancy relaxing during your down time, Tanzania has beautiful beach resorts. You can also take part in exciting watersports including sailing, water skiing and windsurfing.

What volunteering is available in Tanzania?

There is a huge variety of volunteering opportunities. You can help out in hospitals and orphanages. Even if all you can do is serve food, you will still be useful. There are also animal sanctuaries, but these are only open to people with experience of working with animals. A specialist company is a good place to start, as they will match you with the right volunteering position.

Nora Galetti caught the travel bug in

3   Now use the features you found to identify the three types of text.

Text A is a/an ....

Text I is a/an ....

Text J is a/an ....

More types of text

You need to be able to identify the main features of each of the types of text you could come across in the test.

1   What type of information do reports and fact sheets usually contain? Circle the answer you think is correct.

| formal information | informal information | stories |

2   Which **two** of the following statements about reports and fact sheets are true? Put a cross in each boxes you think are correct.

☐   A   They may contain opinions.

☐   B   They always use statistics.

☐   C   They may use charts.

☐   D   They always use pictures.

☐   E   They contain facts and statistics.

☐   F   They try to look exciting.

3   Which **two** features do reports and fact sheets use to make key information easier to find?

....

....

> GUIDED   4   Match the text type to the description. Some statements might match more than one text type.

Tries to persuade a reader to do something   Specification

Contains facts   Leaflet

Uses pictures to look more exciting   Report

Usually laid out in table style   Poster

Often uses statistics   Fact sheet

5   Look at Texts D, E, F and H on pages 77–81 Identify the text type for each one.

Text	Text type
D	....
E	....
F	....
H	....

Texts that inform

Some texts use factual information to inform the reader.

> To work out the purpose of a text, you need to look carefully at:
> * the text type
> * the layout
> * the type of language used.

1   Which of these words might be used in your test instead of the word 'inform'?
    Circle the answer you think is correct.

    persuade   encourage   tell   give

2   Which of the following text types is **most likely** to be used for informative writing?
    Circle the answer you think is correct.

    poster   leaflet   blog

GUIDED 3   Which of the following features are usually used in informative writing?
    Circle the answers you think are correct.

    columns   pictures   coloured fonts   ⟨graphs⟩

    tables   charts   ⟨facts⟩

4   What type of language is usually used for informative writing? Circle the correct answer.

    slang   formal language   text language

5   Look at Text D on page 77. Find and label the features you circled in question 3.

6   Now read the whole of Text D on page 77 and answer the test-style question below.

What is the **main** purpose of Text D?
☐ A   to inform the reader about problems on the High Street
☐ B   to tell the reader what is wrong with the toilets
☐ C   to describe the facilities on the High Street
☐ D   to inform the reader about the litter problem on the High Street   **(1 mark)**

Texts that instruct

The purpose of some texts is to instruct the reader how to do something.

1 Which of the following statements about instruction text is true?
Put a cross in the box you think is correct.

☐ **A** It is found only on packaging and leaflets.

☐ **B** It can be found on almost any type of text.

☐ **C** It is always found in a table.

☐ **D** It needs to be very entertaining.

2 Which of these words might be used in the reading test instead of the word 'instruct'? Circle the answer you think is correct.

explain   describe   tell   encourage

3 Which of the following are usually found in instruction texts? Circle the correct answers.

columns   pictures

slang   numbered lists

command verbs   clear language

4 Look at Text B on page 75. Find the features you identified in question 3 and label them.

5 Now read the whole of Text B on page 75 and answer this test-style question.

What is the main purpose of Text B?

☐ **A**   to explain how to prepare the chocolate for the fountain

☐ **B**   to show how many people can use the fountain

☐ **C**   to explain how high quality the chocolate fountain is

☐ **D**   to instruct the reader what to do if the fountain is faulty

(1 mark)

Texts that describe

Some texts are written to describe. They tell readers what something is like.

1   Which **two** of the following are most likely to contain descriptive writing?
    Put a cross in each box you think is correct.

    ☐   **A**   blogs

    ☐   **B**   articles

    ☐   **C**   reports

    ☐   **D**   websites

    ☐   **E**   fact sheets

‣ GUIDED ⟩   2   Using the words provided, fill in the blanks in the following paragraph about
    descriptive writing.

    .... are often used for descriptive writing rather than

    .... This is because descriptive writing needs to contain

    lots of *extra detail*. A lot of .... are used as

    they help to build up a picture in the reader's mind.

~~extra detail~~	bullet points	paragraphs	descriptive words

3   Read this extract from Text J on page 83. Identify and label any of the descriptive writing
    features from question 2.

    > I think that Tanzania is the most beautiful country in Africa. It has everything from game
    > reserves to jungle-clad mountains. It is home to Mount Kilimanjaro and within easy
    > reach of laid-back Zanzibar. It is a country that has fantastic wildlife viewing, countless
    > walking opportunities and mountain trekking for the more adventurous.
    >
    > If you just fancy relaxing during your down time, Tanzania has beautiful beach resorts.
    > You can also take part in exciting watersports including sailing, water skiing and
    > windsurfing.

4   Now read the whole of Text J on page 83 and answer this test-style question.

    > What is the **main** purpose of the article?
    >
    > ☐   **A**   to describe the beach resorts in Tanzania
    >
    > ☐   **B**   to tell the readers how to volunteer in Tanzania
    >
    > ☐   **C**   to describe what it is like to volunteer in Tanzania
    >
    > ☐   **D**   to tell readers about the watersports in Tanzania
    >
    > **(1 mark)**

Texts that persuade

Some texts are written to persuade readers to believe something or to do something.

1   Which of the following is **least likely** to contain persuasive writing?
    Put a cross in the box you think is correct.

    ☐ **A**   letters

    ☐ **B**   articles

    ☐ **C**   adverts

    ☐ **D**   posters

    ☐ **E**   reports

2   Which of the following words might be used in your test instead of 'persuade'?
    Circle the answers you think are correct.

    encourage   advertise   tell   explain   claim

GUIDED 3   Which of the following are you likely to find in texts that persuade? Circle the answers you
    think are correct.

    tables   charts   detail

    (facts)   statistics   quotations

4   Look at Text F on page 79. Find the features you identified in question 3 and label them.

5   Now read the whole of Text F on page 79 and answer this test-style question.

> What is the **main** purpose of the leaflet?
>
> ☐ **A**   to encourage the reader to learn to cook
>
> ☐ **B**   to tell the reader about European River Cruises
>
> ☐ **C**   to persuade the reader to book a European River Cruise
>
> ☐ **D**   to encourage the reader to try Italian cookery
>
> (1 mark)

Putting it into practice

Now you know how to read a text, and identify the main ideas, the text type and the text purpose. Practise answering the test-style questions below.

> Before writing your answers in the test:
> • Read the questions carefully.
> • Skim read the text to find the main ideas.
> • Underline relevant information in the text.

1   Read Text C on page 76 and answer the test-style question below.

What is the **main** purpose of Text C?

☐ **A**   to tell the reader how to become a plumber

☐ **B**   to inform the reader about new evening courses

☐ **C**   to tell the reader about the College's new IT suite

☐ **D**   to inform the reader about foundation courses   **(1 mark)**

---

2   Read Text E on page 78 and answer the test-style question below.

What is the **main** purpose of the poster?

☐ **A**   to persuade people to use the gym

☐ **B**   to inform people about health and safety in the gym

☐ **C**   to tell people about the gym equipment

☐ **D**   to encourage people to stay fit and healthy   **(1 mark)**

---

3   Read Text G on page 80 and answer the test-style question below.

Identify **two** features from the list below that show that Text G is a letter.

☐ **A**   sections

☐ **B**   logo

☐ **C**   use of 'Dear'

☐ **D**   address and date

☐ **E**   paragraphs

☐ **F**   sub-headings   **(2 marks)**

Understanding presentation

In your reading test you will need to identify a variety of presentation features.

1 Give **two** reasons why writers use presentation features.

....

....

2 Understanding presentation features will help you to identify what **two** things in the test?

....

....

> **GUIDED** **3** List **five** different presentation features.

Columns

....

....

....

....

> You will need to identify presentation features clearly in your test by using the correct name.

4 Look at Text A on page 74. Identify **two** different presentation features.

> You can use your answers to question 3.

....

....

5 Look at Text D on page 77. Identify **two** different presentation features.

....

....

6 Look at Text H on page 81. Identify **two** different presentation features.

....

....

Paragraphs, columns and fonts

You need to understand why some texts use paragraphs, columns and different fonts.

1   Which **two** of the following statements about fonts are true? Put crosses in the boxes you think are correct.

☐   **A**   Fonts are used to separate sentences.

☐   **B**   Font styles and colours often link to the ideas in the text.

☐   **C**   All texts use the same fonts.

☐   **D**   Different font styles are used to make a text look more interesting.

☐   **E**   Bold fonts always mean the words are true.

Look at this extract from Text J and answer questions 2, 3 and 4.

> **So why is Tanzania still my top destination?**
>
> The people in Tanzania are wonderful. They give every visitor a friendly welcome and love to show you their country.
>
> I think that Tanzania is the most beautiful country in Africa. It has everything from game reserves to jungle-clad mountains.
>
> It is home to Mount Kilimanjaro and within easy reach of laid-back Zanzibar. It is a country that has fantastic wildlife viewing, countless walking opportunities and mountain trekking for the more adventurous.
>
> **Nora's top advice**
>
> I am often asked for advice about volunteering. My best piece of advice is – always use a specialist company to organise your trip. It means you have somebody to turn to if anything goes wrong. They will also tell you what vaccinations you need. And vaccinations are important if you don't want to ruin the experience of a lifetime!

2   Why has the writer used paragraphs?

....

....

3   Which of the following presentation features is often used in articles to break up the text and make it easy to read? Circle the answer you think is correct.

fonts   columns   words   colour

4   In the text extract above, label the feature you identified in question **3**.

5   Find **two** texts that use different fonts as a presentation feature.

....

....

Titles, headings and lists

Understanding why texts use titles, headings and lists will help you in your reading test.

GUIDED   **1**   Match the features on the left below to the functions on the right.

Titles   To get a reader's attention

Headings   To separate texts into small pieces

Numbered lists   To give them an idea of what the text is about

Bullet points   To tell the reader the topic of a small section of text

Sub-headings   To make the text easy to follow

2   Complete the following sentence by selecting the correct word from the box below.

Writers use .... to get a reader's attention and then often use

.... to give them an idea of what the text will be about.

numbered lists	titles	bullet points	paragraphs	headings

Look at this extract from Text A and then complete questions 3 and 4.

Why join our tuneless choir?

If you join our tuneless choir you will still get all the health benefits of a regular choir, but:

- there are no scary auditions
- you will be with people who are also tuneless
- you will never have to sing a solo!
- there is always cake at our meetings!

How do you sign up for the Tuneless Choir?

There are just three easy steps:

1. Call Bernie on 0116 952 3881 and ask for an application form.
2. Complete the application form.

---

3   Why do instructions often contain numbered lists?

....

GUIDED   **4**   Write the names of the missing presentation features in the blank spaces below, then draw arrows linking each name to the feature in the text above.

.... : to tell the reader the topic of a small section of text.

bullet points : to separate texts into small pieces.

.... : to make the text easy to follow in order.

Had a go ☐   Nearly there ☐   Nailed it! ☐

Tables and charts

Tables, graphs and charts are used to make information in a text easier to understand.

GUIDED **1** Fill in the gaps in the sentences by selecting words from the boxes below.

Some texts present information in a ...., or use a .... for part

of the information. Tables are often used for factual texts. We use them because they make it

.... to find .... information ....

table	quickly	easy	~~factual~~	chart	relevant

> In the test, it is a good idea to read the whole question before you start. Practise this here by reading all the answer options before filling in any blanks.

Charts present information visually. This makes information easy to find and understand. Look at Text D on page 77 and answer the questions that follow.

GUIDED **2** Write a sentence explaining how you would find the answer to this test-style question using the chart in Text D. The answer has been started for you.

> What was the biggest High Street problem for the people in the survey?
>
> ....
>
> ....
>
> **(2 marks)**

I would look at the size of the bars to ....

....

....

3 According to the chart in Text D, should the council spend money on better parking or on taking action about litter?

....

Had a go ☐   Nearly there ☐   Nailed it! ☐

Images and graphics

Images and graphics are used to make texts more interesting and appealing.

1   Complete the table below by adding the names of the three presentation features.

....	These make texts more appealing or give visual information about a text.
....	These are usually made on a computer. They make a text look more interesting.

> Make sure you learn the correct names for presentation features, as you will need to use them in the test.

2   Which **three** of the following are more precise names for types of graphics? Circle the answers you think are correct.

images   bullet points   logos   headings   captions   diagrams

3   Look at Text B on page 75 and answer the following test-style question.

> Identify **two** presentation features that have been used to make the chocolate fountain seem appealing.
>
> ....
>
> ....
>
> **(2 marks)**

4   Identify two texts from pages 74 to 83 that use images or graphics.

....

....

Putting it into practice

1   Read Text H on page 81 and answer the test-style question below.

> Remember to name features correctly. If one of the features is a picture of a fish, write 'picture' or 'image' – not 'fish'!

Identify **two** features that have been used to make the fact sheet look more interesting.

....

....

(2 marks)

2   Read Text I on page 82 and answer the test-style question below.

Identify **two** features that have been used to make the blog look more interesting.

....

....

(2 marks)

3   Read Text D on page 77 and answer the test-style question below.

Identify **two** features in the report that have been used to make information easier to find.

....

....

(2 marks)

4   Read Text G on page 80 and answer the test-style question below.

Identify **two** features that have been used to make information easier to read.

....

....

(2 marks)

Understanding detail

You should read both texts in your test carefully to make sure you understand the details.

1   Which **two** of the following might you be asked to do? Put crosses in the boxes next to the correct answers.

☐   **A**   Underline the main ideas.

☐   **B**   Label text types.

☐   **C**   Find specific details.

☐   **D**   Find contact details.

☐   **E**   Identify statements that are true.

2   How many of the questions that ask you to find details from the text will be multiple choice? Put a cross in the box you think is correct.

☐   **A**   All of them

☐   **B**   At least one

☐   **C**   None of them

☐   **D**   Some of them

> Remember to read all the questions carefully before you start. If you make a mistake in a multiple choice question, put a line through it clearly and put another cross in the correct box.

Read this test-style question. You do not have to answer it. Look at what it is asking you to do, then answer questions 3 and 4.

> Give one reason why you should join the Tuneless Choir.
>
> ....
>
> **(1 mark)**

3   In the test, which word in the question above would be in **bold**? Underline it.

4   Why would the word be in a bold font?

    ....

5   Read the following test-style questions. You do not need to answer them. In each one, underline key words that would help you find the correct answer.

> **1**   Which **one** of these statements about the Tuneless Choir is true?
>
> ☐   **A**   It was set up in 2010 by Bernie Godfrey.
>
> ☐   **B**   Auditions are held twice a month.
>
> ☐   **C**   It is for those who can't sing aloud in the car.
>
> ☐   **D**   You will be a better singer if you join the Tuneless Choir.   **(1 mark)**
>
> **2**   How can you get an application form for the Tuneless Choir?   **(1 mark)**

> Always make sure you know how many details are required.

Reading for detail

After you skim read the texts, you should then read each text again carefully.

GUIDED

1   To find specific information in a text, you should follow **four** steps. These are listed below. Put them in order by writing the correct number in the box.

☐ Look for key words in the most likely part of the text.

☐ Read the relevant part of the text carefully to find the information you need.

2 Skim read the text to find out where the specific information is likely to be: if the text has sub-headings or a table, look at the headings first.

☐ Read the question carefully to find out what you need to look for.

Read the following extract from Text A. Follow the steps above to answer the test-style questions that follow.

Text A

Have you spent your life being told you are tone deaf? Did a teacher ask you to keep quiet in music lessons at school? Do you only sing out loud when you're alone in the car?

If you answered yes to any of the above questions, then read on. The Tuneless Choir was set up in 2010 by Bernie Godfrey as an alternative to formal choir groups. It is for people like you who avoid singing aloud in public. We welcome anybody, regardless of age, gender or ability. We now have over 60 regular members and meet twice a month in Estrick Church Hall. For the past two years we have given a Christmas Concert in the church.

Why is singing good for you?

You may think you are just standing still, but singing exercises major muscle groups in the upper body. Singing is actually an aerobic activity, as it encourages you to take more oxygen into your body. This leads to increased alertness and is good for your heart and lungs. Singing improves your airflow, which helps to stop viruses like colds and flu. It also helps to develop motor control, particularly for people who suffer with poor circulation.

One of the major benefits of singing is the feel-good factor. Modern life causes stress for many people. It is often the small, everyday things that get people really stressed, such as difficult journeys to work or school. Singing is a fantastic way to get rid of this type of stress. *'It's brilliant for getting rid of worries,'* says our singing coach Janey Smith. *'After singing you feel like you've got a spring in your step. You realise all your worries have just dropped away.'*

---

2   According to the website, singing is good for you. List **one** benefit of singing.

....

3   According to the website, tuneless people often avoid singing aloud in public. List **one** reason why people may feel they are not suitable for a choir.

....

Always read the question and the relevant part of the text carefully. As in question 2 above, sometimes the question may not use the exact words from the text.

27

Careful reading

You should read both texts carefully to make sure you find exactly the right piece of information for each question.

1   What must you do in order to answer multiple choice questions correctly?

....

....

Read the following extract from Text G below. Then answer questions 2 and 3.

> <u>We feel you will lose out on business if you ignore this new system.</u> You have a website where customers can choose their treatments, but they still have to telephone for an appointment. This can sometimes be a problem. If they cannot get through to your salon straight away they may not try a second time. <u>If they have to wait on the phone while an assistant checks a paper diary they may give up.</u> If they are checking the website at a time when you are not open, they may not remember to phone the next day.
>
> The advantages to your customers of our new system are obvious. Customers can see what time slots are available and all appointments can be booked online. Your website is open 24/7, so they can browse for appointments at any time. They will not need to wait on the phone while a paper diary is checked. One of the most important benefits is probably the fact that customers can book appointments from anywhere, even while they are on holiday!
>
> I would also like you to think about the advantages to your business. You can check online to see how many staff you need each day. <u>All your staff members can look at the bookings at the same time, as it is very easy to use.</u> Customers can be prompted to book additional treatments, which will increase your profits. Also, with a paper diary mistakes can be made. Some members of staff have writing that is difficult to read. Sometimes staff members are interrupted when they take a call and forget to record a cancellation. When assistants are very busy they can even record appointments on the wrong day.

2   Three pieces of information have been underlined in the text. Use your answer to question 1 above to find the correct answer to the test-style question below.

> To check your answer is correct, you can rule out each of the other options.

> According to the letter, why will the salon lose business without the online booking system?
>
> ☐   **A**   The system is new.
>
> ☐   **B**   It is easy for all staff to use.
>
> ☐   **C**   Customers do not like to wait on the telephone.
>
> ☐   **D**   Most hairdressers have online booking now.   **(1 mark)**

3   Option D in the test-style question does not contain words or phrases from the text. Even if you know it to be true, why must you **not** select it as the correct answer?

....

Tricky questions

Not all the questions in your reading test will be straightforward to answer.

GUIDED **1** Multiple choice questions can be tricky as some of the wrong answers can seem correct at first glance. What **four** steps should you take to make sure you answer correctly?

1 ....

2 Think carefully about each of the answers in turn.

3 ....

4 You should now be left with the correct answer. Put a cross in the box.

2 Use the four steps above to answer this multiple choice question about Text I on page 82. Put a cross in the box you think is correct.

Which of the following statements about the animal shelter is true?

☐ **A**   Visitors are given a safety briefing as soon as they arrive.

☐ **B**   Sick animals can stay for a short time.

☐ **C**   Sick or injured animals are kept in a separate area.

☐ **D**   All the animals are easily scared.

(1 mark)

3 Now read the final entry in Text I on page 82 Using only the information in the blog, answer the following test-style question.

According to Text I, give **one** reason why you should think carefully before adopting an animal from a shelter.

....

....

(1 mark)

> Remember, even if you know a lot about a topic, you should only use the information you can find in the text to answer a question.

4 If you can't find key words from the question in the text, what should you do?

....

....

Vocabulary

There are several things you can do if you come across an unfamiliar word in your test.

>GUIDED> **1** What should you do if a text uses words you have not seen before? Give **three** steps you should take before checking in a dictionary. The answer has been started for you.

Read the text before and ....

....

....

2 Using the method from question 1, work out the meaning of the underlined words in the extracts below. When you have worked out the meaning, write it in your own words on the dotted lines.

> **Why is singing good for you?**
>
> You may think you are just standing still, but singing exercises major muscle groups in the upper body. Singing is actually an **aerobic** activity, as it encourages you to take more oxygen into your body. This leads to increased alertness and is good for your heart and lungs.

aerobic = ...

> **WARNING TO PARENTS OR GUARDIANS**
>
> Ensure fountain is placed on a secure table or surface before use. Not suitable for dishwashers. This product **complies** with all European and British legislation, making it safe if used correctly.

complies = ...

> Estrick Vocational College was opened in 1994 to provide skilled tradespeople to local businesses. The Building Trades Department was opened in 2011 and now runs over 20 different courses. Two years ago a new IT suite was added to support students with their written **assignments**. Our aim is to prepare students fully for life on a construction site.

assignments = ...

> You could find unfamiliar words in any type of text. Make sure you work out their meaning before rushing into any answers.

Using a dictionary

If you have tried all the techniques on page 30 and are still unsure about the meaning of a word, you can use a dictionary in the test.

1 In what order do the following words appear in a dictionary? Write the numbers 1 to 5 to show the order.

   ☐ importance

   ☐ year

   ☐ alphabetical

   ☐ size

   ☐ star

2 When you have found the section for the first letter of the word, what should you do next?

   ....

3 Use a dictionary to check the meanings of the unfamiliar words you worked out on page 30.
   Did you write the correct definitions? If not, write them here in your own words.

   aerobic   ....

   complies   ....

   assignments   ....

Look up the word **sanctuary** in the dictionary and read the definition carefully.
Read the extract below and answer question 4.

> **What volunteering is available in Tanzania?**
>
> There is a huge variety of volunteering opportunities. You can help out in hospitals and orphanages. Even if all you can do is serve food, you will still be useful. There are also animal **sanctuaries**, but these are only open to people with experience of working with animals. A specialist company is a good place to start, as they will match you with the right volunteering position.

4 Close the dictionary and write the meaning of the word **sanctuaries** here in your own words.

   ....

   ....

> Putting definitions into your own words is a good way to remember unfamiliar words and their spellings. Practise this every time you come across an unfamiliar word before your test. It will add to your vocabulary knowledge.

Putting it into practice

Now that you know how to identify and understand the details in a text, you can answer the questions below.

> Remember to:
> - read the questions carefully
> - underline key words in the questions
> - skim read the text to find the best place to look for information
> - go back and read the text carefully to make sure you find the correct details.

1   Read Text J on page 83 and answer the following test-style question.

According to the text, a specialist company will:

☐ **A** organise sailing, water skiing and windsurfing

☐ **B** help you raise money for equipment

☐ **C** give you a friendly welcome and show you the country

☐ **D** help you to check on travel permits   **(1 mark)**

2   Read Text I on page 82 and answer the following test-style question.

Name **one** activity that is covered in the shelter's safety briefing.

....

(1 mark)

3   Read Text H on page 81 and answer the following test-style questions.

1   According to the text, which of the following statements about the climbing wall is true?

☐ **A**   It cannot be used without a caretaker.

☐ **B**   It has been checked by a qualified Health and Safety Inspector.

☐ **C**   It cannot be used without the correct equipment.

☐ **D**   It is outside the main office building.

2   According to Text H, where are raffle tickets available?

....

(1 mark)

Using information

In the test you will need to show that you understand how to use the information found in a text.

1 Which types of text are useful for convincing people to do something or buy something? Circle the answer you think is correct.

descriptive texts   informative texts   instruction texts   persuasive texts

Look at this test-style question and read Text E on page 78. Then answer the questions below.

> Using the poster, identify **two** things you should do before exercising in the gym.
>
> ....
>
> ....
>
> **(2 marks)**

GUIDED **2** Which **two** of the following answers could be used for the question above?

- ☐ **A** read the instructions for each piece of equipment
- ☒ **B** drink plenty of water
- ☐ **C** warm up
- ☐ **D** put on good trainers
- ☐ **E** check weights are in place
- ☐ **F** speak to a member of staff

GUIDED **3** Why is option D above **not** a correct answer to the test question?

It might be true but ....

....

4 Answer this test-style question.

> Your friend is thinking of joining a gym, and wonders how Estrick Gym can help him to get fit and healthy. According to Text E, in what **two** ways could the gym help your friend to get fit and healthy?
>
> 1 ....
>
> 2 ....
>
> **(2 marks)**

> Always read a text carefully before starting your answer.

Responding to a text

In your test you will need to read the texts carefully and think about how the writer wants you to respond. Some texts want to encourage readers to take action.

Read the test-style question below carefully. You do not need to answer it. Then read the extract below from Text H and answer questions 1–3.

Your friend is thinking about holding an event to raise money for the climbing wall, but needs some help. Using Text H, give **two** ways that the College can help your friend with an event.

1 ....

2 .... **(2 marks)**

1 How can you help?

- You can make donations direct to the College (see our website).
- You can sell raffle tickets (books of tickets are available at reception).
- You can raise sponsorship money through any activity of your choice (for example, a sponsored walk).
- You can take a stall at our fundraising day, e.g. selling homemade cakes or soft toys.

2 How can we help you get started?

Firstly, you can use our buildings and outside areas for your sponsored event. To do this, you will need to speak to our caretaker, who has an office in the main college building. Secondly, you could use our office services for support with printing, photocopying or making telephone calls. Also, you could advertise your event in our weekly newsletter and on our website.

3 What difference will your help make?

We cannot use the climbing wall safely unless we have the correct equipment.
The wall will remain unused until we have all the items above. As soon as we have all the equipment, we will get the wall checked by a qualified Health and Safety Inspector.
The students will then receive training from an experienced climbing instructor.

1   Which of the three paragraphs from Text H would be the best place to look for answers to the test-style question? Circle the answer you think is correct.

    1   2   3

2   Text H also contains information that could persuade readers of the benefits of donating money. Which paragraph would help to persuade a reader to donate to the fund?
Circle the answer you think is correct.

    1   2   3

3   Using the paragraph you chose for question 2, give **two** reasons why readers should donate to the climbing wall fund.

....

....

Putting it into practice

Now you know how to use and respond to the information in a text, practise answering the questions below.

1   Read Text C on page 76 and answer the test-style question below.

> A friend is thinking of applying to start a tiling course at Estrick College.
> Identify **two** things that your friend needs to do before applying.
>
> 1   ....
>
> 2   ....   **(2 marks)**

2   Read Text G on page 80 and answer the test-style question below.

> Your friend is thinking about booking with a hairdressing salon that has an online booking system.
>
> Using the information in the letter, identify **two** reasons why booking a hair appointment online would be a good idea for your friend.
>
> 1   ....
>
> 2   ....   **(2 marks)**

3   Read Text I on page 82 and answer the test-style questions below.

> Your friend wants to volunteer at her local animal shelter, but is worried that she has no experience and will not know what to do.
>
> Using the blog, identify **two** examples to reassure your friend that the shelter offers training to volunteers.
>
> 1   ....
>
> 2   ....   **(2 marks)**
>
> You have a friend who wants to adopt an animal from the shelter, and thinks it will be easy.
>
> Using the information in the blog, give **two** reasons to convince your friend that adopting an animal from the shelter is a serious decision.
>
> 1   ....
>
> 2   ....   **(2 marks)**

Avoiding common mistakes

There are some common mistakes that you can learn to avoid in your reading test.

Look at a student's answer to a test-style question relating to Text B on page 75, then answer the questions below.

> Your friend is considering buying a present for her daughter, who loves chocolate.
>
> Using the information in Text B, give **two** reasons why your friend should consider buying the Cocoa Lover Chocolate Fountain for her daughter.
>
> You do **not** need to write in sentences.
>
> 1   My friend should consider buying a chocolate fountain for her daughter because
>
>   it has been fully tested for children.
>
> 2   Her daughter will like it because you can use marshmallows with chocolate fountains.
>
> **(2 marks)**

GUIDED 1   The student's first answer is correct, but why would it have wasted time in the test?
The answer has been started for you.

Because you don't need to write ....

2   The student's second answer is incorrect. Explain what common mistake the student has made.

....

....

Now go back and read the test-style question again carefully. Then answer questions 3 and 4 below.

3   Underline key words in the question that will help you to find the two correct answers.

4   Now answer the question correctly, avoiding the mistakes the student made above.

....

....

5   Another student has rushed a different test question relating to Text B, below. Read the question carefully, underline any key words and then correct the student's mistake.

> According to Text B, what should you do if any parts of the chocolate fountain are faulty?
>
> Go to the website.
>
> **(1 mark)**

Checking your work

When you have finished answering the questions in your reading test, it is a good idea to go back over your answers to check for mistakes.

GUIDED 1   Give **two** of the most common mistakes students make in the reading test.

1   Giving answers that are too brief

2   ....

2   Which **one** of the two answers below is correct for this test-style question about Text F? Underline the correct answer.

> According to the leaflet, how do you book one of Estrick River Company's cruises?

> go to the company's website and www.estrickrivercompany.com

> www.estrickrivercompany.com

(2 marks)

3   Read the following test-style questions carefully and underline key words. Then read Text F on page 79 and correct the mistakes a student has made when answering the questions.

> 8   The **main** purpose of this leaflet is:
> ☐ A   to tell the reader about the food on river cruises
> ☒ B   to encourage readers to book a river cruise
> ☒ C   to tell the reader what happens on a river cruise
> ☐ D   to encourage readers to take a cookery course   **(1 mark)**
>
> 9   According to the leaflet, which **two** of the following statements are true?
> ☐ A   The company's boats take more than 40 people.
> ☐ B   The company's boats have en-suite facilities.
> ☒ C   The company started over 30 years ago.
> ☐ D   The company offers 15 different cruises.
> ☐ E   The company will be offering cookery courses in 2017.   **(1 mark)**

4   How much time should you save in your test to check your work?

....

Writing test skills

There will be two writing tasks in your Functional Skills writing test. These will assess your writing skills, including spelling and punctuation.

GUIDED 1 Read these explanations of two of the skills you will need in your writing test. Fill the gaps with the words at the bottom of each section. The first one has been started for you.

Write clearly, using detail

Writing clearly means that your language needs to make *sense* and be easy to

.... You will also need to add .... to *develop* your

points. This will ensure your readers have all the necessary or important ....

read	information	~~sense~~	detail	~~develop~~

Present information in a logical order

You must present your writing in a .... order. To do this, you could use

.... if you are writing a letter or an ....

paragraphs	logical	article

2 Give **two** types of text that use headings and sub-headings.

....

....

3 You will need to use language that is suitable for audience and purpose. Identify **one** way you can make sure your language suits your audience and purpose.

....

4 You will need to use correct grammar, spelling and punctuation. Why is it important to punctuate your work correctly?

....

....

5 List **three** types of punctuation.

....

....

....

Writing test tasks

In your test you should read each writing task carefully to make sure you know exactly what you are being asked to do.

Look at this example of a Task 1 test question. You don't need to answer it. Read it carefully and then answer the questions that follow.

TASK F

INFORMATION
You recently stayed for a night at the Estrick Lighthouse Hotel.

You were promised a luxury room with a sea view and a table reserved in the restaurant for 8pm. When you arrived, there were no sea view rooms available so you were given a small room at the back of the hotel that had not been cleaned. No restaurant booking had been made and you were unable to get a meal until after 9.30pm.

You asked to speak to the Hotel Manager but were told he was too busy to see you. The receptionist insisted that you still needed to pay the full price, as the hotel had turned away other bookings in order to give you a room.

WRITING TASK
Write a letter of complaint to Paolo Albero, the Manager of Estrick Lighthouse Hotel, Promenade Street, Estrick, EW12 5HH.

You may wish to include:
- what you had booked in advance of your stay
- what went wrong when you arrived at the hotel
- how you have been treated so far
- what you want to happen now.

---

1   What **three** things should you identify in each task?

....

....

....

2   How do the bullet points in a writing task help with your answer?

....

GUIDED   3   Before you start planning, you will need to know the audience, purpose and format for your writing. In the task above, audience and format have been underlined for you. Underline the purpose.

> Always underline audience, purpose and format for each task. You could do it as you read the question – this will save you time in the test.

GUIDED   4   A student has made some planning notes for the task above. Underline the note that is the most suitable.

- Use formal language as purpose is serious.
- Put it all into one paragraph to be brief.

Putting it into practice

Read this example of a Task 2 test question. You don't need to complete it. Instead, think about what it is asking you to do, then answer questions 1 and 2.

Task C

You and your friends recently spent an enjoyable evening at the Estrick Bistro. As you were leaving, you picked up this card.

ESTRICK BISTRO
High Street, Estrick

High-quality British cooking in a friendly setting

A wide selection of dishes using organic and locally grown produce

Jazz band on Thursday and Friday evenings

Events catered for: weddings, christenings, birthday celebrations

Outside area and children's play area open in the summer months

Bookings taken on **0115 345 4567**

Visit our website www.estrickbistro.com for further information and menus

---

WRITING TASK

Write an email to a friend, suggesting he visits and saying why you had such an enjoyable evening at the Estrick Bistro recently.

- Say what you liked about your evening.
- Say why your friend would enjoy visiting.

You can add any other interesting information.

---

1   Underline the audience, purpose and format for Task C.

2   Plan your answer to Task C by writing notes on the audience, purpose and format.

....

....

....

....

....

....

Understanding audience

It is important to make sure your language is suitable for the intended audience.

Look at this extract from the test-style task on page 92. You don't have to complete it. Read it carefully and think about the audience.

> **WRITING TASK**
> Write an article for your school/college/workplace newspaper, describing your favourite local attraction.
>
> In your article you may want to include:
> * what you find interesting or exciting about the attraction
> * when it is open and how much it costs to visit
> * what it has to offer visitors.
>
> You could add any other useful information.

GUIDED 1 Match the audiences on the left below with the information on the right. One has been done for you.

College student   Sherwood Park – play centre, lake, £2.50 per adult, children free

School student   Local cinema – all-night shows at weekends, licensed café
                           £10, half price for students on Thursdays

Working family man   Bowling alley – disco nights, café, games alley
                           £6 per lane per hour, under-16s discount

Now look at another extract from the test-style task on page 84. You don't have to complete it. Read it carefully and then answer questions 2 and 3.

> **WRITING TASK**
> Write an email to Simon Howells, Manager of Estrick Music Mart.
>
> In your email you should:
> * give details of the singing event
> * persuade him to provide the refreshments.

2 Emails are more informal than letters, but you do not know Simon Howells. Which form of address would be most appropriate? Circle the answer you think is correct.

Dear Mr Howells   Dear Simon

3 Look at the sentences that a student has written in response to the task above. Put a cross next to those that you think are suitable for the audience.

☐ **A** I am writing to you as the owner of Estrick Music Mart.

☐ **B** Be like the Town Council and help us out with this!!

☐ **C** I know you will agree that the Church Hall repair fund is a worthwhile cause.

☐ **D** Simon, we really, really need you to help us with drinks and stuff for this festival.

☐ **E** We have over 50 local people taking part and it is sure to be well attended.

Letters and articles

You could be asked to write a letter or an article in the writing test. You will need to use the correct format for each task.

Look at Task F on page 89. You don't have to complete it. Read it carefully and answer questions 1–4 below.

1   Put your address, the address of the person you are writing to, and the date in the layout boxes below.

....

....

....

....

....

....

....

....

....

2   Which of the following greetings is most suitable for this letter? Put a cross beside the answer you think is correct.

☐   **A**   Dear Martin

☐   **B**   Dear Mr Hughes

☐   **C**   Dear Sir

☐   **D**   Dear Sir or Madam

3   Which of the following sign-offs is most suitable for this letter? Put a cross beside the answer you think is correct.

☐   **A**   Yours sincerely

☐   **B**   Bye

☐   **C**   Thanks

☐   **D**   See ya

4   You could be asked to write an article. Put a cross beside **two** features from the list below that you could use to make your article more interesting and easier to follow.

☐   **A**   Menu

☐   **B**   Address

☐   **C**   Date

☐   **D**   Heading

☐   **E**   Sub-headings

Emails and online discussions

In your writing test, you may be asked to write an email or an internet forum post.

Look at Task D on page 87. Read it carefully and answer the questions below.

GUIDED 1   Which of the following would be the most appropriate way to end the email?
Circle your choice. One incorrect answer has been crossed out for you.

Regards   Thanks   Yours sincerely   B̶y̶e̶

2   What would be a suitable subject heading for your email?

....

Now look at Task B on page 85. Read it carefully and answer questions 3 and 4 below.

3   You need to read the other messages on the internet discussion before you start to write your response. Do you agree with Ellie or Janet? Why?

....

....

....

....

....

....

....

> Even if you don't know very much about the topic, you can use details in the other messages to help you write your response.

4   Begin your own message to add to this internet discussion. Write your name and the date in the correct places. Then write an opening sentence making your views clear. You can use the ideas in your answer to question 3.

....

....

....

....

....

Formal writing

You need to read the writing task carefully to work out how formal your writing should be.

> **GUIDED**

1 List **four** situations where you should use a formal style when writing.

You are applying for a job.

....

....

....

2 Which **two** of the following usually require a formal style? Circle your choices.

letters   emails   articles   internet discussions

> Remember to read the question carefully and underline the audience, purpose and format. These will help you to decide which writing style to use.

3 Which **two** of the following are **not appropriate** for formal writing. Circle the correct answers.

slang   sentences   text language   punctuation   headings

Look at Task G on page 90. Read it carefully and answer the question below.

4 A student has started an answer to this task, but has not used a formal style. Rewrite the start of the letter using a formal style.

> Dear David
>
> I'm writing 'cos there's cars all over the pavement near my house. Last week me mum fell 'cos she couldn't get her shopping trolley past a van. You need to get something done now!!

....

....

....

....

....

Informal writing

Informal writing will be more appropriate for some of the tasks in your writing test.

GUIDED 1   List **four** situations where informal writing would be acceptable.

You are adding your views to an informal discussion.

....

....

....

2   Emails can use an informal style, but you should still use language that is suitable for your audience. Which greeting is most suitable if you do not know the audience? Circle the answer you think is correct.

Hi!   Dear Mr Smith   Hey!   Dear Sir or Madam

Look at Task C on page 86. Read it carefully and answer questions 3 and 4 below.

3   Which of the following would be suitable for the above task? Circle your choices.

contractions   informal phrases   text language   slang   complete sentences

4   A student has started an answer to the task above, but has used a style that is too formal for the audience. Rewrite it, using a more informal style.

> Dear Danny,
>
> I am writing to let you know about the Estrick Bistro which is on the High Street in town. My girlfriend and I visited last night and really enjoyed the high quality British cooking. The bistro uses only organic produce that is local. It also has a good wine list. I do not know anything about wine, but the waiters explained all the choices very carefully.

....

....

....

....

....

....

> Exclamation marks are a good way to show excitement in informal writing. Do not overuse them as they lose impact. A good rule is not to use more than two in a piece of writing.

Putting it into practice

Read this test-style question. Write the **first two** paragraphs of your answer to the task. Focus on using the correct style for audience and purpose, and on using the correct features for the format.

Task F

INFORMATION
You recently stayed for a night at the Estrick Lighthouse Hotel.

You were promised a luxury room with a sea view and a table reserved in the restaurant for 8pm. When you arrived, there were no sea view rooms available so you were given a small room at the back of the hotel that had not been cleaned. No restaurant booking had been made and you were unable to get a meal until after 9.30pm.

You asked to speak to the Hotel Manager but were told he was too busy to see you. The receptionist insisted that you still needed to pay the full price, as the hotel had turned away other bookings in order to give you a room.

WRITING TASK
Write a letter of complaint to Paolo Albero, the Manager of Estrick Lighthouse Hotel, Promenade Street, Estrick, EW12 5HH.

You may wish to include:
• what you had booked in advance of your stay
• what went wrong when you arrived at the hotel
• how you have been treated so far
• what you want to happen now.

You can add any other useful information.

Understanding planning

Read Task C on page 86. You don't need to answer it. Instead, think about what it is asking you to do and answer questions 1 and 2 below.

1   Why is it a good idea to plan before you start answering a writing question?

....

....

2   Underline the key words and phrases in the task information below.

ESTRICK BISTRO
High Street, Estrick

High-quality British cooking in a friendly setting

A wide selection of dishes using organic and locally grown produce

Jazz band on Thursday and Friday evenings

Events catered for: weddings, christenings, birthday celebrations

Outside area and children's play area open in the summer months

Bookings taken on **0115 345 4567**

Visit our website www.estrickbistro.com for further information and menus

---

 3   Complete this plan for the task.

- email to friend = informal style

- write about what will interest him = likes (music and wine)

  - what friend would enjoy – ....

  - what friend would enjoy – ....

- what I liked – ....

- what I liked – friendly waiters

Using detail

Some tasks will not have bullet points. For these tasks you will need to think about what information your audience needs.

1   Which of the following statements about using detail is **not** true? Put a cross next to the correct answer.

☐ **A**   You can use the information section to help you add detail.

☐ **B**   You should only use information in the question to answer the question.

☐ **C**   Using detail helps the audience to understand a text.

☐ **D**   You can use your imagination to add detail to your writing.

Read Task B on page 85. You don't need to answer it. Instead, think about what information the audience will need, then answer the questions below.

2   Think about whether you agree or disagree with the information. Underline any points in the text that you want to agree or disagree with.

GUIDED 3   Now think about what information you could add that will interest the audience. Add detail to each of the points you underlined for question 1. An example has been provided.

- Exercising in fresh air is good, but you need professional help from the gym to get properly fit.

- ....

- ....

- ....

- ....

- ....

Ideas

Some tasks use pictures rather than written information. You can use these to get ideas for your plan.

Look at Task G on page 90. Look carefully at the pictures and then answer the questions below.

 1 Write **four** details you can see in the pictures that provide useful information for your answer. An example has been provided.

People are also leaving bins out, no room between bins and cars

....

....

....

2 Look at a student's thoughts for Task G below. Use your notes from the pictures to add detail to the thoughts. One has been done for you.

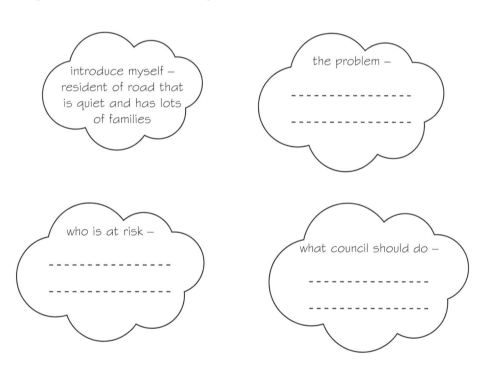

introduce myself –
resident of road that
is quiet and has lots
of families

the problem –
- - - - - - - - - - - - - - -
- - - - - - - - - - - - - - -

who is at risk –
- - - - - - - - - - - - - - -
- - - - - - - - - - - - - - -

what council should do –
- - - - - - - - - - - - - - -
- - - - - - - - - - - - - - -

Putting it in order

Your plan should be in a logical order. Read Task H on page 91. You don't need to answer it now. Instead, think about what information should come first in the article.

A student has made a plan for the task. Read the plan and then:

1   Number the main points from most to least important.

2   Finish the plan by adding details to about what the council should do.

- School sports
- Article – needs title and subheadings
- Probably adult
- Audience so needs to be formal

School is for learning

- Disagree – school is for learning, not sport
- Sport takes time away from English and Maths lessons

Mobile phones

- Mobiles could be used to help young people get fit
- Young people often use phone apps for fitness

After-school sport

- Students can improve fitness after school
- Students can join after-school clubs – better than watching TV

What should the council do?

- ....

- ....

> In the test, you should plan your answer before you start writing. Don't spend too much time on your plan - you need to leave time to add interesting details to your points.

Putting it into practice

Read the test-style task below. You do not have to write an answer. Instead, think about what information the audience will need and then answer the question below.

INFORMATION
You recently stayed for a night at the Estrick Lighthouse Hotel.

You were promised a luxury room with a sea view and a table reserved in the restaurant for 8pm. When you arrived, there were no sea view rooms available so you were given a small room at the back of the hotel that had not been cleaned. No restaurant booking had been made and you were unable to get a meal until after 9.30pm.

You asked to speak to the Hotel Manager but were told he was too busy to see you. The receptionist insisted that you still needed to pay the full price, as the hotel had turned away other bookings in order to give you a room.

WRITING TASK
Write a letter of complaint to Paolo Albero, the Manager of Estrick Lighthouse Hotel, Promenade Street, Estrick, EW12 5HH.

You may wish to include:
• what you had booked in advance of your stay
• what went wrong when you arrived at the hotel
• how you have been treated so far
• what you want to happen now.

You can add any other useful information.

Use the space below to write a plan for the task. Remember to:
• use the bullet points to help you plan your writing
• use the information to add detail
• include details about audience and format
• number your ideas so you can write them in a logical order.

> Remember to spend 5 minutes on your plan in the test. Use this activity to practise writing a plan in 5 minutes.

Using paragraphs

You may want to use paragraphs to structure your writing.

1   Which of the following statements about paragraphs is **not** true? Put a cross next to the correct answer.

☐ **A**   A paragraph is a group of sentences about one topic or idea.

☐ **B**   Using paragraphs helps you to develop your ideas.

☐ **C**   Paragraphs are an effective way of structuring your writing.

☐ **D**   Paragraphs should be three sentences in length.

GUIDED 2   Look at a student's thoughts for Task J on page **93**. Produce a paragraph plan by grouping similar ideas into three separate paragraphs. One has been done for you.

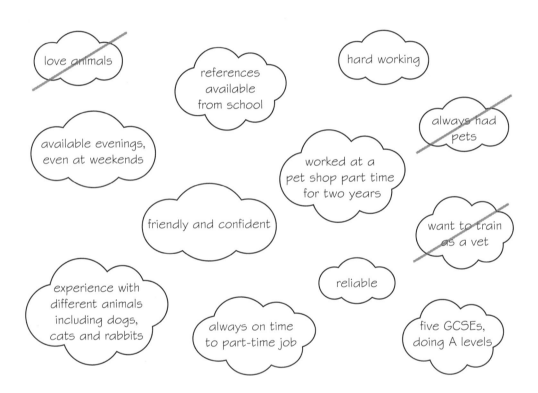

1   Why I want to volunteer:
    love animals
    always had pets
    want to train as a vet

2

3

Point–Evidence–Explain

Point–Evidence–Explain (P.E.E.) can help you to structure your paragraphs and add detail to your writing.

1   Complete the following rules for P.E.E. paragraphs. Use the words in the box below.

The first sentence should contain your .... After your point comes your

.... Evidence is .... This can be more than one

.... if you have a lot of .... to add. After your evidence

you should .... how the evidence backs up your point.

| detail   evidence   sentence   explain   details   point |

> **GUIDED** 2   List **three** things you can use as evidence in your answers. One has been done for you.

facts ....

....

....

> **GUIDED** 3   A student has written a P.E.E. paragraph for Task J on page 93, using the paragraph plan from page 52. Label the point, the evidence and the explanation. One has been done for you.

Why I want to volunteer:
• love animals
• always had pets
• want to train as a vet

I would like to apply as a volunteer because I love animals. I have always had pets since I was a young child and it was my job to look after them. Now it is my ambition to train to be a vet at university. This volunteering job will give me experience that will help me get into university.

point

4   Use P.E.E. to write another paragraph for Task J on page 93. Use your paragraph plan from page 52.

....

....

....

....

....

....

....

Internet discussions

In your writing test you could be asked to write a blog post or forum message. You will need to know the correct structure for both types of text.

1 Which **two** of these statements about writing forum messages and blogs are true? Put a cross beside each answer you think is correct.

☐ **A** You do not need to use Standard English.

☐ **B** You do not need to use detail.

☐ **C** You could just use one paragraph.

☐ **D** You can use any structure you want.

☐ **E** You need to use detail in your writing.

GUIDED 2 A student has written a structured and detailed answer for Task B on page 85. One paragraph has been used and a P.E.E. structure makes it easy to follow. Label each point, the evidence and the explanations. The points have been done for you.

> Tara 20th March 2016
>
> I agree with Ellie. The gym is a complete waste of money. You can easily exercise at home by following a workout on YouTube or by buying an exercise DVD. Then the money you save could be spent on some simple exercise equipment. You will also save time as you don't have to travel to the gym. My nearest gym is in town on a main road, so getting there often takes a lot of time. I use the time I save to exercise for longer. Sometimes I even exercise outside! Like Ellie says, fresh air is great for you and totally free. This is probably my top reason for staying away from a gym!

3 Look at Task A on page 84. A student has made some planning notes and numbered them in a logical order. Use a clear P.E.E. structure to write **one** paragraph.

email, formal as don't know audience
one paragraph
1 singing event, date, 60 people, all giving
up their time
2 need refreshments, know he loves singing
3 good cause, hall used by many groups,
know he's been to concerts there

> Notice that this student has used the information provided with the task but has also added some other details.

....

....

....

....

....

Headings and sub-headings

Headings and sub-headings usually contain important information. You should look at them carefully in the test.

1   Give **two** reasons why writers use headings and sub-headings for articles.

....

....

2   Which **two** of the following statements about headings and sub-headings are true? Put a cross beside each answer you think is correct.

     ☐   **A**   You should underline your headings and sub-headings.

     ☐   **B**   You should use capital letters for all the letters in a heading.

     ☐   **C**   You should only use one sub-heading in an article.

     ☐   **D**   You start headings and sub-headings with a capital letter.

▶ **GUIDED** ⟩   3   There are different ways to write a heading. Match each of the headings below with the reason it is being used. One has been done for you.

To make the topic clear   Is sport being left on the couch?

To ask a question   Sport in, mobiles out!

To make a bold statement   Sport at school

4   Read Task I on page 92, about local attractions. Think of a heading using one of the ways above.

....

5   Each paragraph in an article should have a sub-heading. Think about what the audience will need to know for Task I, and think of **three** sub-headings about your local attraction.

....

....

....

> In your test it is a good idea to leave an empty line before a sub-heading. This will make each of your paragraphs very clear.

6   Why do writers use sub-headings?

....

Lists and bullet points

Lists and bullet points allow you to summarise a lot of detail. They make it easy for the reader to follow your writing.

1   Bullet points make important points easy to read, but they are not suitable for every type of writing.

For which **two** of the following would bullet points be most suitable? Put a cross beside the answers you think are correct.

☐   **A**   a letter of application

☐   **B**   an email to a friend about a day out

☐   **C**   an advert for sports equipment

☐   **D**   a blog entry about healthy eating

Now read Task E on page 88. You don't need to answer it. Just think about what it is asking you to do, then answer questions 2 and 3 below.

> **GUIDED**   2   Bullet points are a good way to present information in an advert. Each of the items in the email can be a bullet point in the advert, but all will need more detail. Write the bullet points.

- Men's running shoes. We have 14 pairs of size 9 men's running shoes. They are brand new and we are only selling them as we need space for new stock. We are selling them for the bargain price of £10 per pair!

- ....

- ....

- ....

> Notice that after the name of the item for sale, the student has used full sentences. You should use complete sentences in your test.

3   Write **two** sentences about what the money raised will be used for. One of your sentences should contain a list.

....

....

....

....

Putting it into practice

Write **two** paragraphs of an answer to Task G on page 90. Focus on structuring your answer. You could use your plan from page 52.

This is a Task 1-style task. You should aim to spend 5 minutes planning for this type of task in the test, then 20 minutes writing and checking your work.

....

....

....

....

....

....

....

....

....

....

....

....

....

....

....

....

....

....

Sentences

Simple sentences make one point and have one verb. A verb is an action word.

1   Underline the **verbs** in the simple sentences below.

    (a)   I will sing a solo.

    (b)   Simon provides the refreshments.

    (c)   I walk to the gym every day.

    (d)   Ben liked the food.

    (e)   I sold the shoes.

    (f)   My friend booked a ticket.

    (g)   The dogs bark loudly.

2   Every sentence needs a verb and somebody or something to do the verb. Look at the sentences in question 1 again and circle *who* is doing the verb.

GUIDED   3   You can add extra details to simple sentences to show when, where or how the action is happening. Add *when*, *where* or *how* detail to the sentences in question 1.

    (a)   I will sing a solo *at the Music Festival*.

    (b)   Simon provides the refreshments ....

    (c)   I walk to the gym ....

    (d)   Ben liked the food ....

    (e)   I sold the shoes *very quickly*.

    (f)   My friend booked a ticket ....

    (g)   The dogs bark ....

4   Which **four** of the following words can be used to link simple sentences into longer sentences? Circle your choices.

    and   is   to   but   the   because   or

GUIDED   5   Complete the following sentences using one of the four linking words you identified in question 4.

    (a)   The Animal Shelter feeds stray dogs *and* makes sure they are healthy.

    (b)   Jane loves to sing .... she is thinking of joining a choir.

    (c)   I liked the food at the bistro .... I felt it was very expensive.

    (d)   The children can walk to school .... they can take the school bus.

    (e)   Ben visits the local cinema often .... it has the best popcorn in town.

    (f)   The room was comfortable .... it did not have a sea view.

> Always check your work carefully to make sure all your sentences make sense. Remember, they must have a verb.

Writing about the present and future

Sentences can be about things that are happening now, things that have already happened and things that will happen in the future. These are called the present, past and future tenses.

1   To write about the present, you need to think about the verb in your sentence. In each of the sentences below, circle the correct verb.

  (a)   We hope / hopes you can donate / donates the refreshments for our festival.

  (b)   I (exercise) / exercises regularly in the fresh air.

  (c)   My friends at the gym encourages / encourage me to try harder.

  (d)   Jim loves / loved Estrick Bistro on the High Street.

  (e)   Dogs bark / barks loudly and frighten / frightens the children.

2   Complete these sentences by adding a suitable verb in the present tense.

  (a)   Sam is very athletic; he .... in the park every day.

  (b)   I .... the bistro on special occasions.

  (c)   When it is raining, we .... the bus to school.

  (d)   Cars .... on the pavement, making it dangerous to .... to school.

  (e)   I hate it when dogs in the park .... near me.

3   Change these sentences to the future tense by using 'going to'.

  (a)   Ben runs in the park at the weekend.

  ....

  (b)   I volunteer in the animal shelter every day in the summer.

  ....

4   You can also use 'will' for the future tense. Write **one** sentence in the future tense using 'will'.

  ....

Always leave a couple of minutes at the end of writing to check your work. Read it carefully to make sure you have used the right tenses.

Writing about the past

You should use the past tense to write about things that have already happened.

1   To write about the past, you need to think about the verb in your sentence. Select the correct verb in these sentences to make them past tense.

(a)   I applied / applyed / applying to do work experience at the sports centre.

(b)   Ellie and I complaind / complained / complain about the poor service in the bistro.

(c)   I filled / filling / fill in an application form to be a volunteer at the animal shelter.

(d)   The team working / workd / worked hard to get the stock ready to sell.

(e)   My friend park / parks / parked his car on the pavement.

> Always think carefully about the verb in a sentence. If the present tense ends in **-e**, you can just add **-d** to make it past tense.

 2   Change the verbs in bold type to make each of these sentences past tense.

(a)   John **try** tried really hard to raise the money.

(b)   I was so scared on the rollercoaster, I **cry** ....!

(c)   We **hurry** .... to finish our meal as the bistro was closing.

(d)   The road is dangerous, so I **carry** .... my daughter to our front gate.

3   Some verbs are tricky in the past tense. Circle the correct verb in each of these sentences.

(a)   John done / did a half marathon for charity.

(b)   We are / were / was late for the sponsored swim.

(c)   I have / had / has a lovely meal at the bistro.

(d)   I see / saw / seen a man jogging in the park.

(e)   Martin was so excited when he get / got / gets a job at the animal shelter.

(f)   I ate / eat / eaten at the college canteen regularly.

(g)   We take / took / taken the long way to the shops.

(h)   It was late when I finally went / gone / go to the supermarket.

> Always check in a dictionary if you are unsure about a past tense. Spend time practising any that you find tricky to remember.

60

Putting it into practice

Write an answer to Task A on page 84.
Make sure you:

• add detail to some of your sentences

• use linking words to join simple sentences

• use the correct tense throughout your answer.

This is a Task 2-style task. You should aim to spend 5 minutes planning for this type of task in the test, then 15 minutes writing and checking your work.

....

....

....

....

....

....

....

....

....

....

....

....

....

....

....

....

....

....

Full stops and capital letters

In your writing test you need to make sure that your sentences have the correct punctuation.

1   When should you use a full stop?

....

2   What should you use at the beginning of each sentence?

....

⟩**GUIDED**⟩   3   List **three** instances when you should use a capital letter.

for proper names like John Smith ....

....

....

4   The pairs of sentences below have been incorrectly separated by commas. They also have some incorrect or missing capital letters. Rewrite them as **two separate** sentences, with full stops and the correct capital letters.

    (a)   estrick music festival starts at 8pm, mrs jones and her daughter janet will sing solos.

....

....

    (b)   I had my Wedding at estrick bistro, a jazz band plays there every saturday night.

....

....

5   These **four** sentences all need some punctuation at the end. Add a full stop, a question mark or an exclamation mark.

    (a)   I was so scared on the rollercoaster I had to shut my eyes

    (b)   I am not happy with the way you have handled my complaint about the room

    (c)   Why should dog owners take their dogs off the lead

    (d)   Do you want to try singing

Commas and apostrophes

Commas and apostrophes are useful to make your writing easy to read.

 1 Put these statements into the correct column in the table below.

Can be used to separate items in a list

Are used to show where letters are missing

Should not be used to separate two different ideas in a sentence ✓

Are used to show that something or someone belongs to someone or something

Commas	Apostrophes
Should not be used to separate two different ideas in a sentence	....
....	....
....	....
....	....

2 Rewrite these sentences, adding commas and 'and' or 'or'.

Cars parked on the pavement will cause problems for children people in wheelchairs mothers with buggies.

....

....

Instead of joining a gym you could try jogging walking swimming using a fitness DVD at home.

....

....

3 Add apostrophes to the following sentences to show who owns what.

> One sentence does not need an apostrophe.

(a) My friends gym charges over £50 a month.

(b) We are selling most of our shops old stock.

(c) Our local school is proud of its sports facilities.

 4 Rewrite the bold words in the sentences below as contractions by removing letters and replacing them with an apostrophe.

(a) I **do not** think anybody should pay to exercise. don't

(b) **I have** had enough of gyms that overcharge. ....

(c) I use a personal trainer at my gym which means **I am** not likely to get injuries. ....

Putting it into practice

Write an answer to Task C on page 86. Focus on punctuation and use:

- one sentence ending with an exclamation mark

- one sentence ending with a question mark

- one sentence containing a list.

....

....

....

....

....

....

....

....

....

....

....

....

....

....

....

....

....

You could use an informal style for this task as it is an email to a friend. This means you could use contractions. Just make sure you don't use too many.

Spelling

There are some spelling tips that will help you to use correct spelling in your writing test.

1   The **i before e rule** helps you to remember the spelling of some difficult words. Use the rule to help you circle the correct spellings in the list below.

believe / beilieve / beleive   deiceive / deceive / decieve

sceince / sceience / science   reciept / reiceipt / receipt

receive / recieve / reiceve   friend / freind / frieind

GUIDED   2   Words with double letters can be difficult to spell. Circle the correct spellings in the list below.

(address) / adresse / addres   dissappoint / disappoint / disapoint

diferent / different / diferrent   possible / posible / posibble

tomorrow / tommorrow / tomorow   dissappear / disappear / disapear

GUIDED   3   A student is having trouble with words ending in **-ly** and words with silent letters. Correct the mistakes the student has made in these sentences. One has been done for you.

(a)   The council needs to take immediate action so that people can cross the road safley.

....

(b)   Your receptionist spoke to me very ~~rudley wen~~ I told her about our room.

Your receptionist spoke to me very rudely when I told her about our room.

(c)   The council is printing the programmes, wich is very kind of them.

....

(d)   I am extremley concerned about the poor fitness of many young people.

....

(e)   The sponsored swim will be on Wenesday.

....

(f)   I booked a room at your hotel as a lovley suprise for my wife.

....

> Very few words end in **-ley**. If you are unsure of a spelling, always check in a dictionary.

Common spelling errors 1

There are common spelling errors that you can avoid in your writing. Some words sound the same but are spelled differently:

there / their / they're

to / too / two

your / you're

we're / wear / where / were

of / off

are / our

 1 Circle the correct spelling in each of the following sentences.

(a) I hope you can provide refreshments for the choir as their / there / (they're) going to be very thirsty.

(b) We are going too / to / two be singing for over to / two / too hours.

(c) The Music Festival is where / wear / we're we perform our / are favourite songs.

(d) Joining a gym costs way to / too / two much money!

(e) Your / you're better off / of exercising in the fresh air.

(f) Some people our / are very critical of what you where / wear / we're at the gym.

(g) Estrick Bistro provided a lovely buffet for are / our wedding reception.

(h) The bistro staff are very proud of there / their / they're good reviews.

(i) If you keep your / you're dog on a lead there / their / they're is no danger of it frightening children.

2 Complete these sentences with the correct versions of the words in question 1.

(a) Children .... at risk because cars are parking on the pavement.

(b) School should be the place .... children learn to take sport seriously.

(c) I don't need to .... expensive gym gear to exercise in the park.

(d) .... is no reason .... pay expensive gym fees when you can exercise outside for nothing.

(e) Our local park is just the place if .... looking for a family day out.

Common spelling errors 2

Some words are often used incorrectly. They can sound similar but are spelled differently:

> would have / could have / should have
>
> bought / brought
>
> write / right
>
> know / no / now

GUIDED 1 Circle the correct word in each of the following sentences.

(a) The council (should have) / should of taken action about the cars on the pavement.

(b) You could of / could have saved money by exercising in the park.

(c) I brought / bought a lot of expensive designer sports gear for going to the gym.

(d) I no / know / now that the council takes this type of problem seriously.

(e) I would of / would have gone to another hotel if it hadn't been so late.

2 Complete these sentences using the correct versions of the words in the box above.

(a) My friend .... his family to Estrick Bistro for lunch.

(b) A lot of injuries .... been prevented if the council had taken action.

(c) I .... you will want to help with the scanner appeal for the local hospital.

(d) It wouldn't be .... to make all dog owners keep their pets on a lead.

(e) Something needs to be done .... about the cars on the pavement.

(f) Children .... a better idea about how to stay fit if they did more sport at school.

> Leave time at the end of your writing tasks to check your work. Make sure all your sentences make sense.

Common spelling errors 3

You should practise spelling words correctly before your writing test.

> Correct spellings can be learned. Every time you spell a word incorrectly, make a note of it and practise the correct spelling regularly.

GUIDED 1   Some of the most frequently misspelled words are in the table below. In each row, one spelling is correct and two are incorrect. Tick the correct spelling and cross out the incorrect spellings.

explanation	exsplanashun	exsplanation
~~feiree~~	~~fierse~~	fierce ✓
althoght	although	allthough
becuse	becos	because
decide	deside	dicide
arguement	argument	argumant
experiance	experence	experience
hapened	happend	happened
bewtiful	beautiful	butiful
interrupt	interupt	intterupt
bisiness	busness	business
menwhile	meanwhile	meenwhile
separate	seperate	seprate
unfortunatly	unfortunately	unfortunitly
queue	que	quew
remembre	remember	remembur
perswade	persade	persuade
straight	strate	straiht
preparation	preperation	preperashun
nervus	nervous	nervos
autumn	autum	awtum
achually	achully	actually

2   Now check your answers on page 68 of the Revision Guide. Use the space below to practise any spellings you are unsure of.

Plurals

Most words can be made into plurals by adding **s**, but there are different rules for words ending in **f**, **fe**, **ch**, **sh**, **x**, **s** and **ss**.

1   Follow the rules to make the bold words in these sentences into plurals. Write the answers on the dotted lines.

   (a)   The **student** .... all passed their fitness **test**. ....

   (b)   There are two interesting **church** .... in my local area.

   (c)   We have several **box** .... of stock to sell this year.

   (d)   We all wrote our **address** .... on the list.

   (e)   My park is beautiful in the autumn when the **leaf** .... fall.

   (f)   One of the many **plus** .... of exercising outside is the fresh air.

GUIDED   2   When words end in **y**, you need to look at the letter before the **y**. Circle the correct plural in these sentences and cross out the wrong one.

   (a)   The park is lovely in the summer, except for the flies / flys.

   (b)   Estrick Bistro has no changing area for babys / babies.

   (c)   Even in the middle of big citys / cities you can find a park to exercise in.

   (d)   I love librarys / libraries because they are so calm and quiet.

   (e)   Parking restrictions should be in place on Sundays / Sundaies.

   (f)   My local swimming pool is ideal for familys / families.

3   Some words look completely different when they are plural. Circle the plurals in the sentences below.

   (a)   The child / children will be very happy with the junior menu.

   (b)   There are always a lot of person / people at my local gym.

   (c)   Most men / man I know prefer to exercise at a gym.

   (d)   Woman / Women should not have to spend a fortune on fancy gym gear.

   (e)   I find exercise really difficult as I think I have two left foot / feet!

> It is a good idea to learn the rules before your test. If there are any words you find difficult you can check them in a dictionary.

Checking your work

It is important to leave time at the end of your writing tasks to check your work.

 1 Look at the extract from a student's writing below. Read it carefully, looking for any errors in:

- spelling

- punctuation

- tense

- sentences, for example misused or repeated words, or incomplete sentences.

Circle and correct all the errors you can find.

Our
(Are) local cinema is the most amazing cinema ive ever been too. it has the biggest screen in

england a brilliant café comfortable seats and the best popcorn you'll ever tasted. Their is a

special childs show on sundays wich is fun as they have games and competitions. I like it becos

they have enough staff so there are never any quwes. Why dont you give it a go this weekend if

your stuck for something too do. believe me, it is definiteley worth a visit.

2 You should always check your work. Go back over your answers to the *Putting it into practice* pages in this book. If you have made any errors like the student above, correct them. Use the table below to list any words you have misspelled and any punctuation and sentence errors you have made.

Spelling errors	Punctuation errors	Sentence errors

> When you have completed the table above you will see what types of mistake you regularly make. Make sure to look out for them in each piece of written work you check.

Putting it into practice

Answer the test-style Task H on page 91 in the space below. When you have finished, check your work carefully. Pay particular attention to the types of mistake you identified on page 70.

....

....

....

....

....

....

....

....

....

....

....

....

....

....

....

....

....

....

This is a Task 1-style question, so spend:

• 5 minutes planning (remember to use the task information and bullet points)

• 20 minutes writing and checking (leave at least 2 minutes to read through and correct any mistakes).

Putting it into practice (example answer)

Look at a student's answer to Task 1 on page 92. Read the comments to see why the student has passed the Functional Skills Level **1** Writing test. Rewrite the student's answer on a separate sheet of paper, making the improvements suggested below.

Like a good film?

What I find interesting
Our local cinema is the most amazing cinema I have ever been too. It has the biggest screen in england, three other screens and a 3D screen. I have been visiting since I was six years old. I still get the same thrill when I walk through the doors. My favourite thing about the cinema is the old-fashioned sweet shop near the entrance. If you're family have a sweet tooth they will love it!

When it is open
The cinema opens every day except Christmas day. It opens at 9am. It shows films all the way through until 11pm. Tickets are £5 for adults and £250 for childs under five. You can buy a season ticket.

What it offers
If you have a family the cinema is perfect for a day out. Your children will love it. They have a special children's show on Sundays with games and competitions. There is a lovely café which serves hot dogs and there is an old-fashioned sweet shop. They also serve lots of different types of coffee.

I can recomend the cinema. Give it a go if your at a loose end on a rainy day.

What has been done well:

✓ Format is correct for an article. It uses a title and sub-headings.

✓ The bullet points from the task have clearly been used to plan the answer.

✓ The student has added detail to each paragraph.

✓ The style is mostly formal, which suits the audience and purpose.

✓ Spelling is mostly accurate.

✓ Punctuation is mostly accurate.

✓ Sentences are complete.

What could be improved:

✗ The sub-headings are not very exciting.

✗ The sentences could be more varied. Several of the simple sentences could be joined with linking words.

✗ There are a few mistakes with words that sound the same, for example your/you're and to/too.

✗ Detail about the sweet shop has been repeated in the first and third paragraphs.

Putting it into practice
(example answer)

Look at a student's answer to Task E on page 88. Read the comments to see why the student has failed the Functional Skills Level 1 Writing test. Rewrite the student's answer in the space provided below, making the improvements suggested below.

FOR SALE

- mens running shoes
- 20 extra large damaged Hooded waterproof jackets
- 5 table tennis sets that include bats, balls and nets
- 25 large Sports towels lots of colours

All 1 pound each. In the shops they would have been 10 pound. money for local hospital scanner.

call mandy on 07785 515423 now as they'll sell fast.

What has been done well:

✓ The correct format has been used for an advert.

✓ Bullet points are suitable for an advert.

✓ Some of the detail from the task information has been used.

What needs to be improved:

✗ Some of the information from the task bullet points has been left out. More detail would make the items sound more appealing.

✗ The information from the task has not been copied correctly. Spelling and punctuation errors have been made.

✗ Not enough detail has been given about price and reason for selling. Incomplete sentences have been used, which makes the advert sound childish.

....

....

....

....

....

....

....

....

....

TEXT A

A friend sent you this.

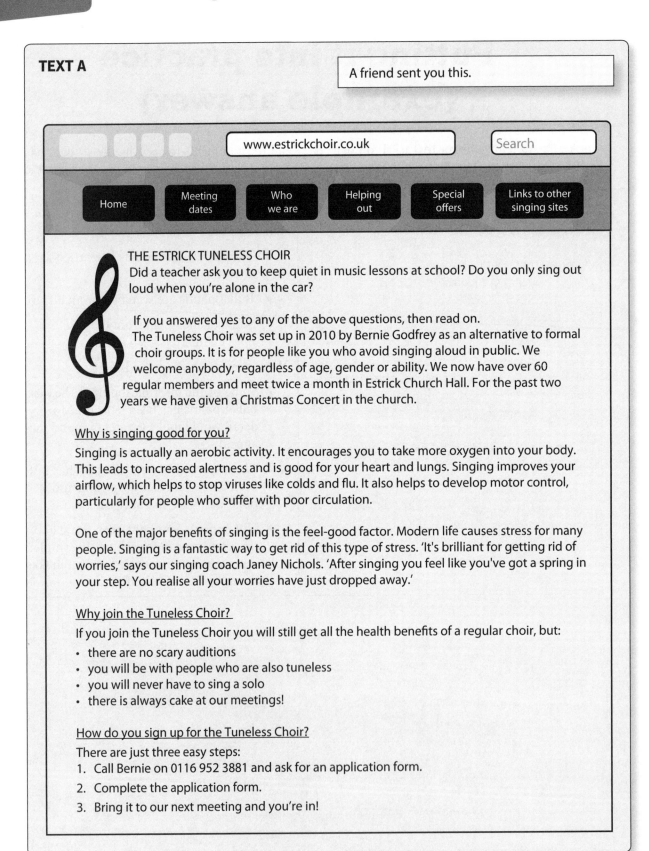

www.estrickchoir.co.uk   Search

Home | Meeting dates | Who we are | Helping out | Special offers | Links to other singing sites

THE ESTRICK TUNELESS CHOIR
Did a teacher ask you to keep quiet in music lessons at school? Do you only sing out loud when you're alone in the car?

If you answered yes to any of the above questions, then read on.
The Tuneless Choir was set up in 2010 by Bernie Godfrey as an alternative to formal choir groups. It is for people like you who avoid singing aloud in public. We welcome anybody, regardless of age, gender or ability. We now have over 60 regular members and meet twice a month in Estrick Church Hall. For the past two years we have given a Christmas Concert in the church.

Why is singing good for you?
Singing is actually an aerobic activity. It encourages you to take more oxygen into your body. This leads to increased alertness and is good for your heart and lungs. Singing improves your airflow, which helps to stop viruses like colds and flu. It also helps to develop motor control, particularly for people who suffer with poor circulation.

One of the major benefits of singing is the feel-good factor. Modern life causes stress for many people. Singing is a fantastic way to get rid of this type of stress. 'It's brilliant for getting rid of worries,' says our singing coach Janey Nichols. 'After singing you feel like you've got a spring in your step. You realise all your worries have just dropped away.'

Why join the Tuneless Choir?
If you join the Tuneless Choir you will still get all the health benefits of a regular choir, but:
- there are no scary auditions
- you will be with people who are also tuneless
- you will never have to sing a solo
- there is always cake at our meetings!

How do you sign up for the Tuneless Choir?
There are just three easy steps:
1. Call Bernie on 0116 952 3881 and ask for an application form.
2. Complete the application form.
3. Bring it to our next meeting and you're in!

TEXT B

You will be helping at a children's party, so you will need to know how the chocolate fountain works.

Age: 10+
Read carefully before using this product.

Cocoa Lover
Chocolate Fountain

An ideal gift for children, or any chocolate enthusiast!

The Cocoa Lover Chocolate Fountain is ideal for parties of up to 10 guests, having a chocolate capacity of 900g.

It has been fully tested, so it is safe to be used by children over the age of 10. It comes complete with melting bowl, mixing spoon, dipping sticks and 5 sachets of chocolate flavouring. All you need to provide is the chocolate.

There is even more fun to be had on our website! More delicious chocolate recipes can be found.

You can enter your best recipes in our monthly chocolate fountain competition!

Get started now!

Contact us on our website at

www.estrickcocoa.com

These instructions are so easy – children can set the fountain up on their own!

You will need:

- large bowl
- small bowl
- chocolate flavouring sachets
- 4 x 125g bars of chocolat

1. Fill the large plastic bowl with warm tap water. Be careful not to use boiling water as this will melt your chocolate too quickly.
2. Break the chocolate into chunks and put it into the small bowl.
3. Put the small bowl into the large bowl. Be careful not to let any water flow into the small bowl.
4. When the chocolate begins to melt, empty one of the flavouring sachets into the small bowl.
5. When the chocolate is fully melted, remove the small bowl and mix the chocolate mixture with the spoon until it is smooth.
6. Pour the mixture into the fountain base.
7. Switch the fountain on and wait 5 minutes before it begins to flow through the machine.
8. Get your marshmallows or fruit ready on the sticks provided and start dipping!

WARNING TO PARENTS OR GUARDIANS

Ensure fountain is placed on a secure table or surface before use. Not suitable for dishwashers. This product complies with all European and British legislation, making it safe if used correctly.

Call our hotline if any part of this product is faulty: 080 952 3881

TEXT C

Estrick College sent you these details.

ESTRICK VOCATIONAL COLLEGE – BUILDING TRADES DEPARTMENT
Specification for new COURSES AVAILABLE 2016/17

Estrick Vocational College opened in 1994 to provide skilled tradespeople to local businesses.

Our aim is to prepare students fully for life on a construction site. This year the college is also introducing some evening classes for those who cannot attend the college full-time.

As we are the only dedicated Building Trades Department in the South East, we attract students from a very wide area. If travel is a problem, help can be given with transport costs. Help is also available for tuition costs for those on a low household income.

All applicants must contact the Main College Office on 0113 515437 to get an application form.

The table below gives brief details of our new evening courses.
Students on courses marked with * are entitled to help with the cost of tools.

Course	Details	Entry requirements
*Foundation course in plumbing	The course develops practical skills in all aspects of plumbing, including hot and cold water and domestic heating. All lecturers are experiences, and in the second year students are supported by qualified plumbers. This two-year course will provide the foundation to start a career in plumbing.	C grade GCSEs in Maths and English. At least two more GCSEs including one in a Design Technology subject such as Resistant Materials.
Decorating	This one-year course will provide practical training in both house and commercial decorating. You will be supported on this course by local decorating professionals.	No qualifications necessary. Driving licence and own car would be an advantage, as some sessions are run outside of the college.
*Foundation course in electrical installation	This one-year course prepares students to start an apprenticeship in electrical installation. By the end of the year you will be working at a professional standard and have a basic understanding of inspection and testing, electrical science and health and safety. The course is split into half theory and half practical.	5 GCSEs at C grade, including Maths and English. Resistant Materials GCSE would be an advantage.
Tiling	One of our most popular evening classes, this course will teach you all you need to know about tiling. Courses run over 12 weeks. There will be a £5 charge per session to cover the cost of materials. Hardship grants are available if needed.	This course is intermediate level and not suitable for complete DIY beginners. Contact on 0347 674810 to check you are ready before applying for this course.

TEXT D

You are doing work experience at your local council offices, and have to print copies of this for the staff.

To: District Council Members
From: Chairman, Estrick Districk Council
Date: December 2015

REPORT INTO SHOPPING FACILITIES IN ESTRICK HIGH STREET

I am able to present to you the results of my investigations into the shopping facilities in Estrick High Street. It is clear from these investigations that improvements need to be made.

Shops & Restaurants

There are many different types of shops on the High Street including a small supermarket, a newsagent, an optician and two banks. Over 50% of the shop spaces available are empty. This is stopping top retail chains from coming to Estrick, as they do not want to be next to an empty shop unit. It is also encouraging vandalism.

The High Street has only one café, which is only open in the mornings. The High Street's only restaurant is due to close down at the end of this year.

Roads & Parking

The High Street itself is pedestrian-only. There is not enough parking close to the shops, which means shops are struggling to attract people to visit the area by car. Parking is only allowed on surrounding streets for 30 minutes and queues of waiting cars cause traffic problems. We have tried to extend this parking time, but residents are now asking for all surrounding streets to be resident parking only.

Pavements

The High Street pavement has not been resurfaced for over 5 years. It is now in very poor condition with many uneven and broken paving slabs. Residents also use the street for dog walking, so dog mess is an issue. There are only two bins on the whole length of the High Street, and complaints have been made about litter.

Facilities

The library closed last year due to lack of funds. The building is now empty. The public toilets are only open for two hours in the morning, due to lack of cleaning staff. Only one bus now operates near the High Street.

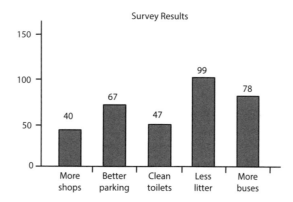

Suggested Council action

Our survey results show that action is required as soon as possible. We do not have the money to undertake all the issues this year, but I think we should do the following now:

1. Provide more litter bins and dog mess bins.
2. Allow buses to enter and stop on the High Street.
3. Start charging for the toilets so that we can pay for cleaning.

TEXT E

You see this on a visit to your local gym.

HEALTH & SAFETY IN THE GYM

50% of gym injuries are caused by incorrect or careless use of equipment. Please follow these simple rules to make sure no one gets hurt while using the equipment

- Use a spotter when lifting the weights.
- Read the instructions for each piece of equipment before using.
- Tell a member of staff if any equipment is damaged or not working.
- Always return weights to the rack after use.

Exercise is a good way to keep fit and healthy. Make sure you think about your health at all times when using the gym:

- Always wipe down equipment before and after use.
- Drink plenty of water when exercising.
- Warm up before exercising.
- Don't exercise if you are unwell or injured.

Our swimming pool is available free for all gym members. Please follow these simple rules to make sure all members can enjoy the pool safely:

- Do not take any food or drink into the pool area.
- Wear a bathing cap if you have long hair.
- Do not use the pool if there is no lifeguard on duty.
- Do not dive into the pool.

The sauna is located next to the pool and is available for all members over the age of 18. Please remember the following when using the sauna:

- Do not stay in the sauna for longer than 30 minutes.
- Do not use the sauna if you are pregnant or unwell.
- Always sit on a towel when in the sauna.
- Try to keep conversation to a minimum – the sauna is a quiet zone.

Safety in the gym is very important. To keep yourself healthy and injury-free in the gym:

- Ask a member of the gym staff to show you how the equipment works.
- Ask one of our personal trainers to work out an exercise programme for you.
- Join one of our fitness classes to learn how to exercise safely.

Estrick Gym

By phone: 021 908 7654

By e-mail: estrickgym@estrick.net

TEXT F

This was delivered through your letterbox.

European River Boat Company Cookery tours

The European River Boat Company started with one narrow boat over 30 years ago. Now, we have 15 boats touring the rivers of Europe. We are the biggest European river cruise operator. As none of our boats takes more than 20 guests at any time, you are guaranteed personal service of the highest possible standard. All rooms on board have en-suite facilities and free wi-fi. The décor is stylish and all the rooms are spacious.

If you have a passion for food and wine, we have added some exciting cookery cruises to our programme for 2017. All courses are taught by top European chefs. Five tours will be available:

- 3-night Top Chef cookery cruise
- 2-night short break featuring Italian cookery
- 3-night wine-tasting cruise
- 3-night introduction to cooking with spices
- 3-night 'Cook the World' luxury cruise.

Typical daily programme:

- 7–9am – buffet breakfast
- 9.30am – yoga on deck
- 10am – on-board lecture from a top chef
- 11am – cookery instruction from a top chef
- 1pm – lunch: eat what you have made
- 4pm – behind-the-scenes tour of local restaurant kitchen OR film show in the bar
- 6pm – back on board for drinks & dinner
- 8pm – dancing on deck

We have a 98% satisfaction rating. Read what two customers have said about our cruises.

Mrs Pirolini of Northampton said: 'The tour was absolute heaven from start to finish. My husband could already cook well, but now he is almost a professional!'

Mrs Wlodarczyk of Estrick said: 'The food was out of this world, the guided tours were well organised and interesting and the boat was luxurious. The best river cruise we've ever done!'

We hope this has tempted you to try one of our cruises. To book, visit our website:

www.estrickrivercompany.co.uk

TEXT G

> Your local hairdresser received this in the post.

Miss Tracey Adu
Manager, Creations Beauty Salon
41 High Street
Estrick
E1 4PS

Estrick Technics
2 North Park Industrial Estate
Estrick
ES4 8PQ
14th January 2016

Dear Tracey

Online Booking Systems

Thank you for your interest in our online booking system. I understand you are not sure of the benefits of an online booking system. I hope that I can give you all the information you need to make up your mind.

We feel you will lose out on business if you ignore this new system. You have a website where customers can choose their treatments, but they still have to telephone for an appointment. This can sometimes be a problem. If they cannot get through to your salon straight away, they may not try a second time. If they have to wait while an assistant checks a paper diary, they may give up. If they are checking the website at a time when you are not open, they may not remember to phone the next day.

The advantages to your customers of our new system are obvious. Customers can see what time slots are available and all appointments can be booked online. Your website is open 24/7, so they can browse for appointments at any time. They will not need to wait on the phone while a paper diary is checked. One of the most important benefits is probably the fact that customers can book appointments from anywhere, even while they are on holiday!

I would also like you to think about the advantages to your business. You can check online to see how many staff members you need each day. All your staff members can look at the bookings at the same time, as it is very easy to use. Customers can be prompted to book additional treatments, which will increase your profits. Also, with a paper diary mistakes can be made. Some members of staff have writing that is difficult to read. Sometimes they are interrupted when they take a call and forget to record a cancellation. When assistants are very busy they can even record appointments on the wrong day.

I really hope this has encouraged you to think about our electronic booking system. Please telephone me on 07457 674810 or visit our showroom if you need further information.

Yours sincerely

Ben Smith

Manager

TEXT H

Estrick College sent you this fact sheet.

CLIMBING WALL FACT SHEET

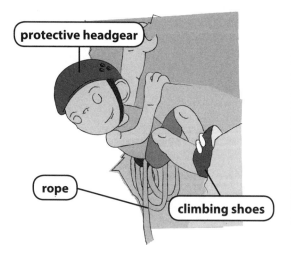

protective headgear

rope

climbing shoes

Also needed:

- ✓ Lockers for equipment
- ✓ Chalk bags
- ✓ Climbing chalk
- ✓ Harnesses
- ✓ Waterproof clothing
- ✓ Safety mats

Dear Supporter,

Thank you for offering to help us raise the money to buy the equipment needed for our new climbing wall. This is an exciting opportunity to provide challenging exercise for the students!

How can you help?

- You can make donations direct to the College (see our website).
- You can sell raffle tickets (books of tickets are available at reception).
- You can raise sponsorship money through any activity of your choice (for example, a sponsored walk).
- You can take a stall at our fundraising day, e.g. selling homemade cakes or soft toys.

How can we help you get started?

Firstly, you can use our buildings and outside areas for your sponsored event. To do this you will need to speak to our caretaker, who has an office in the main college building. Secondly, you could use our office services for support with printing, photocopying or making telephone calls. Also, you could advertise your event in our weekly newsletter and on our website.

What difference will your help make?

We cannot use the climbing wall safely unless we have the correct equipment. The wall will remain unused until we have all the items above. As soon as we have all the equipment, we will get the wall checked by a qualified Health and Safety Inspector. The students will then receive training from an experienced climbing instructor.

We appreciate your support. Go to our website www.estrickcollege.sch.uk to find out more or to donate online.

Jane Edwards

Head Teacher, Estrick College, College Lane, Estrick

TEXT I

> Your friend thought you might find this interesting.

ANIMAL MAGIC BLOG

FIRST DAY!

Posted on April 2nd

Well, I did it! Today was my first day volunteering at the shelter and I loved every minute! I had a safety training session as soon as I arrived. This taught me everything from how to enter a dog kennel and how to handle a small mammal to how to wear my gloves correctly! I then went on a tour to learn about how the shelter works. Did you know that most animals are here because they are just abandoned on the roadside? A few come in because their owners can't manage them any more. Some even come for a short time when their owners are ill or away. We look after them all and try to get them back to full health.

Leave a reply:

TAKING AN ANIMAL HOME!

Posted on April 27th

Lots of my friends have asked me how they can adopt an animal from the shelter. I have found out loads about the process during the past month. You will need to be interviewed to find out what type of animal would suit your lifestyle. The interview also lets people know that adopting an animal needs serious thought. For one thing, I always remind my friends how expensive most animals are to look after. You will need to buy food, bedding and perhaps a cage. You will need to think about vet's bills for all animals, and training classes and grooming if you adopt a dog. It all adds up! Finally, I've learned that pets need time and attention from their owners. You can't just dump an animal in your house and leave it alone!

Leave a reply:

SIGN UP TO MY NEWLETTERS!

Archive:
- March
- February
- January
- December
- November

TEXT J

> You read this in your college library.

WANT TO GIVE SOMETHING BACK? TRY VOLUNTEERING!

By Nora Galetti

Nora Galetti caught the travel bug in her late teens. She now spends 6 months every year volunteering in some of the poorest areas of the world. Here, she tells us why Tanzania is still her top volunteering destination.

So why is Tanzania still my top destination?

The people in Tanzania are wonderful. They give every visitor a friendly welcome and love to show you their country.

I think that Tanzania is the most beautiful country in Africa. It has everything from game reserves to jungle-clad mountains.

It is home to Mount Kilimanjaro and within easy reach of laid-back Zanzibar. It is a country that has fantastic wildlife viewing, countless walking opportunities and mountain trekking for the more adventurous.

If you just fancy relaxing during your down time, Tanzania has beautiful beach resorts. You can also take part in exciting watersports including sailing, water skiing and windsurfing.

What volunteering is available in Tanzania?

There is a huge variety of volunteering opportunities. You can help out in hospitals and orphanages. Even if all you can do is serve food, you will still be useful. There are also animal sanctuaries, but these are only open to people with experience of working with animals. A specialist company is a good place to start, as they will match you with the right volunteering position.

What you need to do before volunteering

Most people use a specialist company to set up their volunteering experience. They can help you to check what type of travel permit you will need.

Nora's top advie

I am often asked for advice about volunteering. My best piece of advice is – always use a specialist company to organise your trip. It means you have somebody to turn to if anything goes wrong. They will also tell you what vaccinations you need. And vaccinations are important if you don't want to ruin the experience of a lifetime!

> If you fancy spending your next holiday helping out in Tanzania, visit the Volunteers Are Us website. It has a list of specialist companies that can help you organise your trip.

TASK A

This is an example of a Task 2 test question.

INFORMATION

You are a member of a choir that is about to take part in a music festival. You receive the email below from the choir's leader.

✉ Send   📎 Attach   💾 Save   ⚪⚪⚫

From:	Bernie (bernie@mailbox.com)
To:	You (you@youmail.co.uk)
Subject:	Estrick Music Day!

Font ☐   12 ☐   **B**   *I*   U̲

Hi,

Just to let you know that we are now booked to take part in the Estrick Music Festival on Wednesday 10th June. We are hoping that all 60 choir members will take part. Four people will sing solos and the rest of us will sing the backing vocals. The admission charge will be £5 per person and all the money raised will go towards repairs on the Church Hall.

The good news is that Estrick Town Council has kindly offered to print our music sheets for us. However, as we are going to be singing for over two hours it would be great if we could have some refreshments. I think Simon Howells of the Estrick Music Mart may donate some for us.

Can you get in touch with Simon and try to persuade him to provide these refreshments? Don't forget to mention that the Church Hall is a great cause. It is used every day by different local groups, from the Scouts to Mums & Tots. It also provides a safe place for teenagers to gather and socialise in the evenings. Don't forget to tell him that four different local choirs will be taking part!

Simon's email address is s.howells@estrickeats.net.

I know you will do a great job for us!

Bernie

WRITING TASK

Write an email to Simon Howells, Manager of Estrick Music Mart.
In your email you should:
- give details of the singing event
- persuade him to provide the refreshments.

(10 marks)

TASK B

This is an example of a Task 2 test question.

INFORMATION

Read the following contributions to an internet discussion about gym membership.

www.fitnesschat.co.uk   Search

Fitness Chat

Ellie   **7th March 2016**

…in my view it is a total waste of money. Why bother paying a monthly fee that you can't really afford when you can exercise for free at home or outside in the fresh air? You would save time if you exercised at home as you don't need to travel to the gym. You can also wear anything you want rather than buying expensive designer fitness gear. It is even better to exercise outside. It is free, but most importantly you will be breathing lots of lovely fresh air!

Janet   **9th March 2016**

Ellie, I totally disagree! It might cost money to join a gym, but you get so much for your money! I have a personal training plan put together by an experienced personal trainer. This means I am not likely to get injured and don't try exercises that I am not yet ready for. I have made lots of friends at the free fitness classes, and we encourage each other to work harder each time we go. I also get exercise outside as I walk to my local gym, breathing that lovely fresh air all the way!

Response

WRITING TASK

Write your own message to this internet discussion, giving your detailed views on the subject of where to exercise.

Use sentences and write in Standard English.

(10 marks)

TASK C

This is an example of a Task 2 test question.

INFORMATION

You and your friends recently spent an enjoyable evening at the Estrick Bistro. As you were leaving, you picked up this card.

ESTRICK BISTRO
High Street, Estrick

High-quality British cooking in a friendly setting

A wide selection of dishes using organic and locally grown produce

Jazz band on Thursday and Friday evenings

Events catered for: weddings, christenings, birthday celebrations

Outside area and children's play area open in the summer months

Bookings taken on **0115 345 4567**

Visit our website www.estrickbistro.com for further information and menus

---

WRITING TASK

Write an email to a friend, suggesting he visits and saying why you had such an enjoyable evening at the Estrick Bistro recently.

- Say what you liked about your evening.
- Say why your friend would enjoy visiting.

(10 marks)

TASK D

This is an example of a Task 2 test question.

INFORMATION
You noticed this in your local newspaper.

Estrick News
8 March 2016
Letter of the week

Dear Editor,

I live near a park where lots of people walk their dogs. I like dogs but I don't think they belong in a park. Dogs need space to run free and should be taken to open spaces outside of towns where this is possible.

Also, many dogs are let off their leads as soon as they get inside the park gates. This is dangerous as the park is used by young families and elderly people out for a stroll. Many people are frightened of animals and their enjoyment of the park is ruined when dogs rush up to them and bark.

I think all parks should be made into dog-free zones.

WRITING TASK
Write an email to editor@estricknews.org, giving your views on the letter.
You may wish to include:
*   where and when you saw the letter
*   your views on the content of the letter.

(10 marks)

TASK E

This is an example of a Task 2 test question.

INFORMATION
You are doing work experience at a local sports shop and receive this email from your manager.

☒ Send   ⏚ Attach   ▣ Save   ● ● ●

From: Zeta (zeta@mailbox.com)

To: You (you@youmail.co.uk)

Subject: Stock sale advert

Font [ ]   12 [ ]   **B**   *I*   U̲

Hi!

Thanks for working over the weekend to help us clear out our stockroom. We now have loads of old stock that needs selling quickly. I have decided to donate the money raised to the local hospital scanner appeal, so that should help it sell.

Can you write the advertisement for this stock, please? I can then put it into the local paper:
- 14 pairs of size 9 men's running shoes
- 20 extra-large hooded waterproof jackets (these have some damage to the sleeves but are still wearable)
- 5 table tennis sets that include bats, balls and nets
- 25 large sports towels, various colours.

Thanks! I know you are good at this type of writing!

Zeta

WRITING TASK
Write the text for the advert, describing the equipment.
In your advert you may wish to include:
- a detailed description of the items
- your reason for selling
- the price you are asking for the items
- the fact that the money will go to charity
- how buyers can contact the shop.

(10 marks)

TASK F

This is an example of a Task 1 test question.

INFORMATION

You recently stayed for a night at the Estrick Lighthouse Hotel.

You were promised a luxury room with a sea view and a table reserved in the restaurant for 8pm. When you arrived, there were no sea view rooms available so you were given a small room at the back of the hotel that had not been cleaned. No restaurant booking had been made and you were unable to get a meal until after 9.30pm.

You asked to speak to the Hotel Manager but were told he was too busy to see you. The receptionist insisted that you still needed to pay the full price, as the hotel had turned away other bookings in order to give you a room.

WRITING TASK

Write a letter of complaint to Paolo Albero, the Manager of Estrick Lighthouse Hotel, Promenade Street, Estrick, EW12 5HH.

You may wish to include:
* what you had booked in advance of your stay
* what went wrong when you arrived at the hotel
* how you have been treated so far
* what you want to happen now.

You can add any other useful information.

(15 marks)

TASK G

This is an example of a Task 1 test question.

INFORMATION

You are getting concerned about the number of cars on your road that are parked on the pavement. This is dangerous, as people are having to walk in the road to get to the local primary school, health centre and community hall.

WRITING TASK

Write a letter to Eva Cabrera, Head of the Environment Department, Estrick Council, Main Street, Estrick, ES1 3MS, to inform him of this problem.

In your letter you should:
*   introduce yourself
*   describe the problem
*   explain who could be at risk
*   say what you want the council to do about it.

Remember to set out your letter correctly.

(15 marks)

TASK H

This is an example of a Task 1 test question.

INFORMATION
You notice this letter in your local newspaper.

Estrick News
20 January 2016
Letter of the week

Dear Editor,

I am very concerned that young people do not seem to take part in regular sports lessons at school. I think too many young people sit around all day with their mobile phones, and this will lead to major health problems when they are older.

School is a good place to show young people how to exercise and get fit. We should make all school children do one full hour of exercise every day at school. They could do this instead of having morning and afternoon breaks.

Yours sincerely,

Anonymous

WRITING TASK
Write an article for the newspaper, giving your views on the subject.
In your article, you should:
* state whether you agree or disagree with the letter
* say why you agree or disagree
* give the reasons that support your views.

You can add any other interesting information.

(15 marks)

TASK I

> This is an example of a Task 1 test question.

INFORMATION

Your school/college/workplace is putting together a guide to local attractions. You have been asked to contribute an article about your favourite local attraction. You should make it sound interesting to visit. You should also include details about opening times, prices and what type of visitor might find it attractive.

WRITING TASK

Write an article for your school/college/workplace newspaper, describing your favourite local attraction.

In your article you may want to include:

- what you find interesting or exciting about the attraction
- when it is open and how much it costs to visit
- what it has to offer visitors.

You could add any other useful information.

(15 marks)

TASK J

This is an example of a Task 1 test question.

INFORMATION

You see this advertisement online and decide to apply.

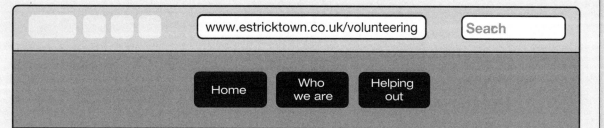

www.estricktown.co.uk/volunteering   Seach

Home   Who we are   Helping out

Volunteers required – Estrick Animal Shelter

We are looking for volunteers to help out in the Animal Shelter at weekends. Applicants must be animal-lovers who are not afraid of hard work. Previous experience working with animals would be useful, but full training will be given to all volunteers. We have many sick and injured animals in the shelter, and they need attention round the clock, so applications from volunteers who can work during the evenings are particularly welcome.

If you are interested in applying, please send a letter to the manager:

Estrick Animal Shelter, River Street, Estrick EN1 4HH.

WRITING TASK

Write a letter to the manager of Estrick Animal Shelter, offering your services as a volunteer. In your letter you should:
- explain why you are writing
- explain why you want to volunteer and why you would be suitable
- give details of your experience.

You may add any other ideas you have.

(15 marks)

Practice paper: Reading

This practice paper has been written to help you practise what you have learned and may not be representative of a real exam paper.

45 minutes

The total mark for this paper is 20.

INSTRUCTIONS
- Use **black** ink or ball-point pen.
- Answer **all** questions.
- Answer the questions in the spaces provided – there may be more space than you need.
- You do not need to write in sentences

SECTION A

Read Text A and answer questions 1–7.

Text A

You read the following article in Estrick News Daily.

Estrick News Daily	14th July 2016

Never too late to start!

By Health Correspondent
Ali Sawalha

'Adults of all ages are not getting enough exercise', claims a top NHS consultant. Professor George Godfrey goes on to argue that most adults spend too long sitting on sofas watching TV, or surfing the internet.
He warns that our modern lifestyle means we are not spending enough time simply moving about.

However, Professor Godfrey is hoping to reverse this trend by launching a new fitness app called 'Just Move a Little'.
He explained that the app is, 'very simple to use, reminding users to get up and move for 5 minutes out of every hour'. The app will beep every 55 minutes and make exercise suggestions.

The benefits of regular exercise are well reported. The government recommends that adults exercise for 30 minutes at least 3 times a week. Even for those over the age of 70 regular walking or gardening is recommended as an easy way to keep active. However, Professor Godfrey insists that even short bursts of activity can improve the heart function of an adult over the age of 45.

'The app is simple to use and comes with instructions for 20 exercises that can form part of a simple 5-minute workout routine. It can be downloaded onto a mobile phone, tablet or even a laptop.

'Regular updates will be available to stop users getting bored with the same old exercise workout.

'Five minutes is enough to get the heart beating faster' says Professor Godfrey, 'and everybody can spare five minutes to look after their health'. His research suggests that three 5 minute bursts of activity each day can help to prevent the onset of diabetes and high blood pressure.

So what are you waiting for! Get the app and just move a little!

Visit the website, www.justmovealittle.com for more advanced exercises and lots of information about how to build exercise into your daily routine.

Answer questions 1 to 3 with a cross in the box. If you change your mind about the answer, put a line through the box and then mark your new answer with a cross.

1   The **main** purpose of this article is to:

☐   A   tell the reader how adults spend their time

☐   B   inform the reader about the new fitness app

☐   C   tell the reader how to use the new fitness app

☐   D   encourage the reader to take regular walks.

(Total for Question 1 = 1 mark)

2   According to Text A, the fitness app:

☐   A   comes with 20 exercises

☐   B   beeps every 30 minutes

☐   C   lasts for 5 minutes

☐   D   beeps 3 times every week.

(Total for Question 2 = 1 mark)

3   According to Text A, which **one** of these statements about adults is true?

☐   A   Adults over 70 watch too much TV.

☐   B   Adults over 70 do too much gardening.

☐   C   Adults are recommended to exercise 3 times a week.

☐   E   Adults are recommended to do 30 minutes of exercise every day.

(Total for Question 3 = 1 mark)

4   How can you find out how to build exercise into your daily life?

....

(Total for Question 4 = 1 mark)

5   List **two** features of Text A that help to present information.

....

....

(Total for Question 5 = 2 marks)

6   Your friend does not believe that short bursts of activity will make any difference to his health. Find **two** pieces of information from Text A to convince your friend that doing short bursts of exercise will help him stay fit and healthy.

....

....

(Total for Question 6 = 2 marks)

7   Your friend is concerned that the app will be difficult to use. Find **two** reasons why your friend will find the app easy to operate.

....

....

(Total for Question 7 = 2 marks)

SECTION B

Read Text B and answer questions 8–13.

Text B

You look on the Estrick Running Club's website.

www.estrickrunners.co.uk   Search

| Home | Healthy living | Estrick Runners | Leisure Centres | Contact the Council |

Estrick Runners

For the last year, Estrick Council have funded experienced runners with first aid training to accompany groups of local residents on 5, 10 or 15k runs. The groups run through parks or countryside and only the 15k involves any hills. The runs take place on Wednesday and Thursday evenings and Saturday mornings.

If you are a complete beginner to exercise, or if you are returning from an injury, you may feel that a 5k run is completely beyond you. However, our new short course will be ideal for you. A guide will take you on a gentle 20-minute jog through lovely parkland at a pace that will suit even those who haven't moved from their armchair in years! There will be plenty of stops along the way and opportunities to get useful healthy living tips from your guide. It will be a very sociable occasion and our runners usually celebrate the end of a run by visiting the café in the park.

These beginners' runs will take place on Saturday mornings and will start at the Memorial in the Estrick Pleasure Park. Simply turn up and start to enjoy the benefits of our guided running scheme, which include:
- A sensible workout overseen by exercise professionals
- The chance to get useful tips on healthy living
- A chance to make some great new friends

You will need to dress appropriately and have good running shoes. A waterproof jacket is a good idea and a bottle of water is essential. We have a locked unit in the Pleasure Park where you can leave any valuables during your run.

When you feel confident enough to join the 5k runners you will be given a unique barcode bracelet that will record your time for every run. So come and join our friendly crew next Saturday!

Follow the link on this page to contact us for further details.

8 The **main** purpose of Text B is:

☐ **A** to encourage the reader to run 5k

☐ **B** to persuade the reader to join a beginners' guided run

☐ **C** to give the reader advice about running

☐ **D** to tell the reader about the benefits of running 5k

(Total for Question 8 = 1 mark)

9 Identify **two** features from the list below to show that Text B is a web page.

☐ **A** bullet points

☐ **B** bold heading

☐ **C** images

☐ **D** website address

☐ **E** links to other pages

☐ **F** punctuation

(Total for Question 9 = 2 marks)

10 Identify **two** things from Text B that you should take with you for a guided run.

....

....

(Total for Question 10 = 2 marks)

11 Your friend does not think he is fit enough to join an organised running event.
Using Text B, give **two** reasons why the Estrick beginners' guided run would be suitable for your friend.

....

....

(Total for Question 11 = 2 marks)

12 According to Text B, how do you take part in the beginners' guided run?

....

(Total for Question 12 = 1 mark)

13 Your friend is considering joining one of the Estrick guided runs but is concerned about health and safety. Using the information in Text B, give **two** points to convince your friend that Estrick Council uses experienced guides who are able to look after all runners.

....

....

(Total for Question 13 = 2 marks)

Practice paper: Writing

This practice paper has been written to help you practise what you have learned and may not be representative of a real exam paper.

45 minutes

The total mark for this paper is 20.

INSTRUCTIONS
- Use **black** ink or ball-point pen.
- Answer **both** tasks.
- Answer the tasks in the spaces provided – there may be more space than you need.
- You will be assessed on spelling, punctuation and grammar in both tasks.

Task 1

Information

You live near Estrick beach. Overflowing rubbish bins outside many of the fast food outlets on the beach are becoming a real problem.

You have heard that the council intends to cut the number of rubbish collections from two per week to just one. You are concerned that this will create a serious health hazard, particularly as young families visit the beach.

Writing Task

Write a letter to Laila Suess, Environmental Officer, Estrick Council, Main Street, Estrick, ES1 3SW.

In your letter you should:

- say why you are writing
- explain the problems the reduction in rubbish collections will cause
- say what you want the council to do about the situation.

Remember to set your letter out correctly.

Use sentences and write in Standard English.

(15 marks)

Task 2

Information

Estrick Town Football Club is small, but very well supported each week. The Club has recently started a youth football club and already has over 50 members. Parents are very enthusiastic about the new youth football club as it keeps their children from spending too long indoors playing computer games. The club would like to enter two teams into a local league but has no more money to buy kit.

Writing Task

As a member of the Estrick Town Supporters Club, you decide to take action. You send an email to Danny Jones, Manager of Estrick Sports, asking him to consider sponsoring the youth teams by providing the kit.

In your email you could:

- give the reason for writing the email
- explain why the Estrick Youth Football Club deserves sponsorship.

You may include any other useful information to persuade the Manager of Estrick Sports to sponsor the team by supplying the kit.

Use sentences and write in Standard English.

(10 marks)

Write your answers to tasks 1 and 2 in the space provided below. You may use extra paper to complete your answers if you need to.

....
....
....
....
....
....
....
....
....
....
....
....
....
....
....
....
....
....

ANSWERS

READING

1. Your reading and writing tests

1 C

2 2

3 2

4

Planning Task 1	5 minutes
Writing and checking Task 1	20 minutes
Planning Task 2	5 minutes
Writing and checking Task 2	15 minutes

5 Answers could include any two of the following:
- Read the question.
- Skim read the text looking for any key words that appear in the question.
- Underline any useful information in the question.

2. Reading test skills

1 topic

2 letter/advert/newspaper article

3 Identify the main points and ideas and explain how they are presented in a variety of texts

Text titles often make the main idea of a text clear. Writers use different ways to present texts to help readers find information easily. For example, a writer might use headings, sub-headings and bold fonts.

Read and understand texts in detail

Writers develop their main ideas by adding detail.

Use the information you find in texts

Readers use the information in texts in lots of different ways. For example, texts can be used to persuade people to do something, or to inform people about how to do something.

Identify how to respond to a text

Texts often ask for some sort of action from readers. For example, a text might ask readers to sign up for further information, or it might ask readers to write a letter of reply.

3. Multiple choice questions

1 Put a line through the box and mark new answer with a cross.

2 The question needs one answer and the student has given two.

3 two

4 A, B and C

4. Short response questions

1 A

2 B is incorrect because writing full sentences wastes time.

C is incorrect as you may need to look at the whole of the text to find an answer.

D is incorrect as it depends on the size of your handwriting – the lines are just a guide.

3 The key word in the question is 'support' but the answer has focused purely on help with costs. Two examples are given in the text of how students receive support with their studies (IT suite, qualified plumbers).

The student has also used full sentences which wastes time in the test.

4 Bold is used to highlight important information in the question, such as how many answers are needed.

5. Reading the question

1 Answer is given on page 5.

2 In multiple choice questions, some options start with the same words or phrases.

3 Your friend does not think that safety is important when he goes to the gym.

Using Text E give **two** reasons why your friend should think about safety in the gym.

4 No, because you should use only the information given in the text.

6. Skimming for ideas and details

1 Answer is given on page 6.

2 They suggest that the letter's purpose will be to inform readers about the benefits of online booking systems.

3 Read the question first.

4

Question number	1	2	3	4
Paragraph number	5	2	4	3

7. Underlining

1 Key words in the question that also appear in the text.

Important information, such as facts and figures.

2

Your friend wants to go on a European river cruise, but does not think he will like any of the boats.

Using Text A, give **two** reasons why your friend might enjoy a European river cruise.

1 Guaranteed personal service of the highest possible standard

2 Décor is stylish and all the rooms are spacious

The European River Boat Company started with one narrow boat over thirty years ago.

Now, we have 15 boats touring the rivers of Europe. We are the biggest European river cruise operator. As none of our boats takes more than 20 guests at any time, you are guaranteed personal service of the highest possible standard. All rooms on board have en-suite facilities and free wi-fi. The décor is stylish and all the rooms are spacious.

If you have a passion for food and wine, we have added some exciting cookery cruises to our programme for 2017. All courses are taught by top European chefs.

3 7–9am – buffet breakfast

9.30am – yoga on deck

10am – on-board lecture from a top chef

11am – cookery instruction from a top chef

1pm – lunch: eat what you have made

4pm – behind-the-scenes <u>tour of local restaurant kitchen</u> OR <u>film show in the bar</u>

6pm – back on board for drinks & dinner

8pm – <u>dancing on deck</u>

8. Online tools 1

1 Answers could include any two of the following:
- so you don't waste time during the test
- so that you know how to read the test clearly and easily online
- so that you know what all the icons do.

2 **Help icon:** You can click this icon if you want a demonstration of how the online test buttons work.

Previous and Next icons: These buttons move you from question to question.

Quit icon: Be very careful with this icon. If you click on it and then click on 'Yes', you will not be able to return to the test, even if you haven't finished!

Time You can click this icon to find out how much time you have left in your test. The time will appear in the bottom left corner of the screen.

3 **Zoom reset:** This takes the text back to the original size.

Colour reset: This takes the text back to the original colour.

Arrows: Use these to move around the page when you are zoomed in.

9. Online tools 2

1 Answer could include one of the following:

Make a plan for answering the writing questions.

Underline key words and phrases in reading texts.

2 For example:

Underlining icon: This button can be used to underline headings.

Right aligned icon: This button can be used to put an address on the right-hand side of the page for a letter.

3 You can Flag a question and then return to it later using the Review button.

4 B

5 Febuary, peice and autum are all spelled incorrectly.

6 i, jenny, liverpool and mr ronaldo should all have initial capital letters

10. Putting it into practice

1 Information underlined should include:

For question 1:

I think that Tanzania is the most beautiful country in Africa. It has everything from game reserves to jungle-clad mountains. It is home to Mount Kilimanjaro and within easy reach of laid-back Zanzibar. It is a country that has <u>fantastic wildlife viewing, countless walking opportunities and mountain trekking for the more adventurous.</u>

For question 2:

There is a huge variety of volunteering opportunities. You can help out in hospitals and orphanages. Even if all you can do is serve food, you will still be useful. There are also animal sanctuaries, but these are only open to people with experience of working with animals. A specialist company is a good place to start, <u>as they will match you with the right volunteering position</u>.

I am often asked for advice about volunteering. My best piece of advice is – always use a specialist company to organise your trip. <u>It means you have somebody to turn to if anything goes wrong. They will also tell you what vaccinations you need.</u> And vaccinations are important if you don't want to ruin the experience of a lifetime!

For question 3:

If you fancy spending your next holiday helping out in Tanzania, <u>visit the Volunteers Are Us website</u>. It has a list of specialist companies that can help you organise your trip.

2. Answers could include:
- Improve underlining to make it more relevant to question.
- Underline only enough to answer the question.

11. Understanding the main idea

1 A

2 Answers could include: title, heading or first few sentences.

3 Arrow from bold font to **50% of gym injuries**

Arrow from images to man lifting weights, woman drinking water etc.

Arrow from title to 'Health & Safety in the Gym'

Arrow from bullet points to list beginning 'Use a spotter when lifting weights' or 'Always wipe down equipment before and after use'

4 poster

5 To instruct

12. Identifying the main idea

1 What the shopping facilities are like in the High Street

How to stay safe and get healthy in the gym

What cookery tours are available

2 The first paragraph suggests that the main idea will be what it is like to work in an animal shelter.

3 The title suggests that the main idea is to describe or explain online booking systems.

The first paragraph suggests that the main idea is how online booking systems can benefit businesses.

13. Identifying types of text

1 Answers could include:
- letters have addresses and emails have 'to' and 'from' boxes
- letters have several paragraphs but emails usually have only one paragraph.

2 Text A

Search box

Navigation bar

Links to other pages on the website

Link to website's home page

Website title

Text I

Blog title

Posting date

Reply/comment box

Text J

Heading

Paragraphs

Sub-heading

Columns

3 Text A is an article.

Text I is a blog.

Text J is a web page.

14. More types of text

1 Formal information

2 C & E

3 Headings and sub-headings

4

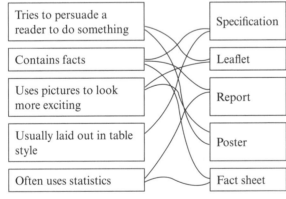

Tries to persuade a reader to do something		Specification
Contains facts		Leaflet
Uses pictures to look more exciting		Report
Usually laid out in table style		Poster
Often uses statistics		Fact sheet

5

Text	Text type
D	Report
E	Poster
F	Leaflet
H	Fact sheet

15. Texts that inform

1 Tell

2 Leaflet

3 Tables and charts

4 Formal language

5 Arrow from facts to 'Over 50% of the shop spaces available are empty.'

Arrow from tables to chart labelled 'Survey Results'

6 A

16. Texts that instruct

1 B

2 Explain

3 Pictures, numbered lists, command verbs

4 Arrow from pictures to image of chocolate fountain or equipment

Arrow from numbered lists to number 1

5 A

17. Texts that describe

1 A & B

2 Paragraphs are often used for descriptive writing rather than bullet points. This is because descriptive writing needs to contain lots of extra detail. A lot of descriptive words are used as they help to build up a picture in the reader's mind.

3 There are descriptive words, such as beautiful and laid-back.

The text includes extra detail, such as 'It is a country that has fantastic wildlife viewing, countless walking opportunities and mountain trekking for the more adventurous.'

The text is separated into paragraphs.

4 C

18. Texts that persuade

1 E

2 encourage and advertise

3 detail, quotations, statistics

4 Arrow from facts to 'The European Boat Company started with one narrow boat over 30 years ago.'

Arrow from detail to bullet list at end of column 1

Arrow from quotations to 'said' in column 2

5 C

19. Putting it into practice

1 D

2 B

3 C & D

20. Understanding presentation

1 To make texts easy to read.
To make texts eye-catching.

2 Type of text and purpose of text

3 Paragraphs, bullets, sub-headings, images

4 Title/paragraphs/sub-headings/images/bullets/numbered list

5 Title/paragraphs/sub-headings/images/chart/numbered list

6 Title/labelled image/bullets/paragraphs/sub-headings/different fonts

21. Paragraphs, columns and fonts

1 B & D

2 To split writing into smaller sections as each paragraph is about a different topic.

3 Columns

4 Columns should be identified.

5 Answers could include texts B, E, F, H or I

22. Title, headings and lists

1.

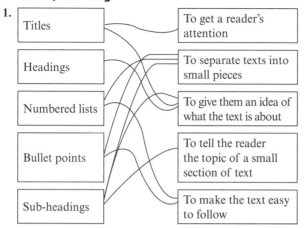

2 Writers use <u>titles</u> to get a reader's attention and then often use <u>headings</u> to give them an idea of what the text will be about.

3 To make the instructions easy to follow

4 Sub-heading

To tell the reader the topic of a small section of text.

Bullet points

To separate texts into small pieces.

Numbered list

To make the text easy to follow in order.

(Arrows should be drawn to correct features.)

23. Tables and charts

1 Some texts present information in a <u>table</u>, or use a <u>graph</u> for part of the information. Tables are often used for <u>factual</u> texts. We use them because they make it <u>easy</u> to find <u>relevant</u> information <u>quickly</u>.

Tables have <u>rows</u> and <u>columns</u>. To read a table, look down the columns to find the <u>section</u> you need and then along the <u>top row</u> to narrow your search.

2 I would look at the size of the bars to find the tallest, then I would look at the bottom row to find out which problem the bar related to.

3 Taking action about litter.

24. Images and graphics

1

Images	These make texts more appealing or give visual information about a text.
Graphics	These are usually made on a computer. They make a text look more interesting.

2 Images/logos/diagrams

3 Different, interesting font; an image

4 Answers could include texts A, B, D, E, F, G, H, I or J

25. Putting it into practice

1 Answers could include: labelled image/bullet points/title/font/sub-headings/checklist in text box

2 Answers could include: images/different fonts/title/headings/text boxes

3 Answers could include: sub-headings/graph/numbered list

4 Answers could include columns, bullet points, headings and sub-headings

26. Understanding detail

1 C & E

2 B

3 The word 'one' should be bold.

4 To remind you to select write only one answer.

5 1 Which **one** of these statements <u>about the Tuneless Choir is true</u>?

2 <u>How</u> can you get an <u>application form for the Tuneless Choir</u>?

27. Reading for detail

1 3, 4, 2, 1

2 Answers could include any one of the following: singing exercises major muscles, singing is an aerobic activity, singing improves airflow, singing gets rid of stress.

3 Answers could include any one of the following: they may have been told they are tone deaf, a teacher may have told them to keep quiet.

28. Careful reading

1 Read all the answer options and the text very carefully, then rule out each incorrect answer.

2 C

3 Because the answer does not come from information given in the text.

29. Tricky questions

1 Read the question again carefully.

Think carefully about each of the answers in turn.

Cross out those that are definitely wrong.

You should now be left with the correct answer. Put a cross in the box.

2 C

3 Answers could include either of the following: pets are expensive/pets need time and attention.

4 Look for words with a similar meaning (synonyms).

30. Vocabulary

1 Read the text before and after the word looking for clues.

Think about whether it looks like any other words you know the meaning of.

Look at any images near the text.

2 For example:

aerobic – something that exercises your heart and lungs

complies (with) – satisfies

assignments – tests or assessments

31. Using a dictionary

1 2, 5, 1, 3, 4

2 Look at the second letter of the word.

3 Meanings should be similar to those for previous page.

4 For example: sanctuaries = places of safety/refuges/protected reserves

32. Putting it into practice

1 D

2 Answers could be any one from: how to enter a dog kennel/how to handle a small mammal/how to wear gloves correctly/how to go into cages quietly

3 C; at reception

33. Using information

1 Persuasive texts

2 A & C

3 It is not a correct answer because it does not come from information given in the text.

4 Answers could include any two of the following:
- The gym staff could show him how the equipment works so he can use it to get fit.
- One of the gym's personal trainers could work out an exercise programme for him.
- He could join one of the gym's fitness classes to learn how to exercise safely .
- He could get fit by going swimming – use of the pool is free to all members.

34. Responding to a text

1 2

2 3

3 Answers could include:

The wall cannot be used without equipment.

The wall will remain unused until all equipment has been bought.

35. Putting it into practice

1 Contact Pete Edwards.

Contact main college office for an application form.

2 Answers could include any two of the following: they can book at any time, they don't need to hold on the phone, they can book from anywhere.

3 Safety training is given

Tours of the shelter are given

Answers could include two of the following:

You need to be interviewed.

Pets are expensive.

Pets need a lot of time and attention.

36. Avoiding common mistakes

1 Because you don't need to write in sentences.

2 The answer might be true, but it is not based on information from the text.

3 Key words should be underlined.

4 Answers could be any two of the following:

It has been fully tested for children.

You can share recipes on the website.

It comes with bowls and other equipment.

You can enter competitions on the website.

It is ideal for parties.

5 Call the hotline.

37. Checking your work

1 Giving answers that are too general

2 The first answer is correct.

3 B, D & F

4 5 minutes

WRITING

38. Writing test skills

1 **Write clearly, using detail**

Writing clearly means your writing needs to make sense and be easy to read. You will also need to add detail to develop your points. This will ensure your readers have all the necessary or important information.

Present information in a logical order

You must present your writing in a logical order. To do this, you could use paragraphs if you are writing a letter or an article.

2 Texts that inform or instruct commonly use headings and sub-headings, so answers could include any two of the following: newspaper article, report, leaflet, poster, fact sheet, recipe

3 Answers could include one of the following:

Choose appropriate vocabulary for the audience

Use the correct form of address in a letter or email

Use formal writing if audience is not known

Use Standard English in a formal text

4 To ensure your meaning clear.

5 Answers could include three of the following: apostrophe, exclamation mark, question mark, full stop, comma, colon, semi-colon

39. Writing test tasks

1 Audience, purpose and format.

2 They help with ideas and structure.

3 The word 'complaint' should be underlined in the question.

4 First bullet point should be underlined.

40. Putting it into practice

1 Write an article for the newspaper, giving your views on the subject.

In your article, you should:
- state whether you agree or disagree with the letter
- say why you agree or disagree
- give reasons that support your views.

Write an email to a friend, suggesting he visits and saying why you had such an enjoyable evening there recently.

2 For example:

Task C is an example of a Task 2 test question	
Timing	20 minutes: plan for 5, write for 15
Notes about audience	Email to a friend can be informal
Notes about purpose	Use lots of details to make place sound exciting
Notes about format	Use heading & paragraphs

41. Understanding audience

1

College student	Local cinema – all-night shows at weekends, licensed café
	£10, half price for students on Thursdays
School student	Bowling alley – disco nights, café, games alley £6 per lane per hour, under-16s discount
Working family man	Sherwood Park – play centre, lake
	£2.50 per adult, children free

2 Dear Mr Howells

3 A, C & E

42. Letters and articles

1 Sender's address should be in top right box, date in box under that with address of person being written to in the left-hand box.

2 B

3 A

4 D & F

43. Emails and online discussions

1 Regards

2 Dogs don't belong in parks (or similar). There's no need for a complete sentence.

3 Students' answers will vary, but need to outline relevant views that they would include in their response to the internet discussion.

4 Date should be on right and name on left.
Example opening sentence:

Janet, I completely agree with you about gyms!

44. Formal writing

1 You are applying for a job.

You do not know your audience well.

your purpose is official.

you are writing to somebody official.

2 Letters and articles

3 Slang and text language

4 For example:

Dear Mr Edwards
I am writing because I am very concerned about the parking on my road. Last week my mother fell over as she could not get her shopping trolley past a van. It needs dealing with urgently.

45. Informal writing

1 You are adding your views to an informal discussion.

Your purpose is to be friendly.

You know your audience personally.

You are using an informal format.

2 Dear Mr Smith

3 Contractions, informal phrases and complete sentences

4 For example:

Hi Danny
I'm emailing to tell you all about the new Bistro. Gemma and I went last night and it was great. The food is wicked

as it's all organic and there's loads of good wine. I don't know much about wine but the waiters all helped me out!

46. Putting it into practice

1 Dear Mr Hughes
I am writing to complain about a recent stay at your hotel. I booked in advance so that I could have a luxury room and a reserved table in the restaurant.

I was very disappointed when I arrived as we were given a small room at the back of the hotel. It had no view and it had not been cleaned. We also did not have a restaurant reservation. We were told we would not be able to eat in your restaurant until past 9.30pm.

47. Understanding planning

1 To make sure your writing is suitable for the audience, purpose and format

2 Make sure you have underlined all the key words and phrases in the task.

3 What friend would enjoy – jazz nights

What friend would enjoy – local grown produce

48. Using detail

1 B

2 Plans could include:

> Points to answer:
>
> **Ellie 7th March 2016**
>
> …in my view it is a total waste of money. Why bother paying a monthly fee that you can't really afford when you can exercise for free at home or outside in the fresh air? You would save time if you exercised at home as you don't need to travel to the gym. You can also wear anything you want rather than buying expensive designer fitness gear. It is even better to exercise outside. It is free, but most importantly you will be breathing lots of lovely fresh air!
>
> Points to agree with:
>
> **Janet 9th March 2016**
>
> Ellie, I totally disagree! It might cost money to join a gym but you get so much for your money! I have a personal training plan put together by an experienced personal trainer. This means I am not likely to get injured and don't try exercises that I am not yet ready for. I have made lots of friends at the free fitness classes and we encourage each other to work harder each time we go. I also get exercise outside as I walk to my local gym, breathing that lovely fresh air all the way!

3 For example:
- Exercising in fresh air is good, but you need professional help from the gym to get properly fit.
- You don't get injuries if you are supervised by professionals.
- You can wear anything you want at the gym, it's not a fashion parade.
- Gyms are better as you have support from others.

49. Ideas

1 For example:

You can't see traffic coming as cars block the view.

You can't walk on the other side as cars block both pavements.

Some cars take the whole pavement so you have to walk on the road.

2 Plan should include notes from question 1.

50. Putting it in order

Plan should be fully numbered and include additional details about what the council would do.

51. Putting it into practice

Plans should use the bullet points in the question as headings and the information section for detail. Plan should be fully numbered into an order that is logical for the audience and purpose and include notes about writing style.

52. Using paragraphs

1 D

2 Letter should explain why you are writing, why you want to volunteer and why you would be suitable, and also give details of your experience.

Example paragraph plan:

1 Why I want to volunteer:
- love animals
- always had pets
- want to train as a vet

2 Why I am suitable:
- hard working
- always on time to part-time job
- five GCSEs, doing A levels
- available evenings, even at weekends
- references available from school

3 My experience:
- worked at pet shop part-time for two years
- experience with different animals including dogs, cats & rabbits

53. Point–Evidence–Explain

1 The first sentence should contain your <u>point</u>. After your point comes your <u>evidence</u>. Evidence is <u>details</u>. This can be more than one <u>sentence</u> if you have a lot of <u>detail</u> to add. After your evidence you should <u>explain</u> how the evidence backs up your point.

2 facts, opinions, statistics

3 I would like to apply as a volunteer because I love animals. [point] I have always had pets since I was a young child and it was my job to look after them. [evidence] Now it is my ambition to train to be a vet at university. This volunteering job will give me experience that will help me get into university. [explanation]

4 For example:

I have some experience of working with animals. Last year I worked in my local pet shop every Saturday. I cleaned out the cages and made sure all the animals had food and water. This will mean I can be useful in the Animal Shelter straight away.

54. Internet discussions

1 C & E

2 Tara   20th March 2016

I agree with Ellie. The gym is a complete waste of money. [point] You can easily exercise at home by following a workout on YouTube or by buying an exercise DVD. [evidence] Then the money you save could be spent on some simple exercise equipment. [explanation] You will also save time as you don't have to travel to the gym. [point] My nearest gym is in town on a main road, so getting there often takes a lot of time. [evidence] I use the time I save to exercise for longer. [explanation] Sometimes I even exercise outside! [point] Like Ellie says, fresh air is great for you and totally free. [evidence] This is probably my top reason for staying away from a gym! [explanation]

3 For example:

I am emailing you about a singing event we are holding on 10th June. Over 60 will be taking part. Four people are going to sing solos so it should be a great event. We hope this means that we will raise a lot of money for the repairs to the Church Hall. We are allowed to use the Hall without charge but we still need some refreshments. I know that you like singing and like to support musical events. I am hoping that for these reasons you will agree to provide the refreshments. The Church Hall is in a terrible state at the moment. This is a shame as it is used by many groups like the mums and tots, the Scouts and the Guides. I know you have been to concerts there so I am sure you will want to help us.

55. Headings and sub-headings

1 They make the topic clear.
They make it sound interesting.

2 A & D

3

To make the topic clear	Sport at school
To ask a question	Is sport being left on the couch?
To make a bold statement	Sport in, mobiles out!

4 Answers will vary.

5 Answers will vary.

6 To show the topic of each paragraph

56. Lists and bullet points

1 C & D

2 For example:

Hooded waterproof jackets. We have 20 extra-large jackets. They have some damage to the sleeves but they are still a bargain at £5 each!

3 For example:

The money raised from this sale will be donated to the local hospital scanner appeal. The hospital is a national centre for the treatment of kidney disease, heart problems and children's cancers.

57. Putting it into practice

Answers should include:
- a clear P.E.E. structure
- paragraphs for each new idea
- a sentence containing a list.

58. Sentences

1 & 2
  (a) I will sing a solo.
  (b) (Simon) will provide the refreshments.
  (c) (I) walk to the gym every day.
  (d) (Ben) liked the food.
  (e) (I) sold the shoes.
  (f) My (friend) booked a ticket.
  (g) The (dogs) bark loudly.

3 For example
  (a) I will sing a solo *at the Music Festival*.
  (b) Simon will provide the refreshments at the Festival.
  (c) I walk to the gym every day after my breakfast.
  (d) Ben liked the food at the local Bistro.
  (e) I sold the shoes *very quickly*.
  (f) My friend booked a ticket at the train station.
  (g) The dogs bark loudly before they go for a walk.

4 and, or, but, because

5 (a) The Animal Shelter feeds stray dogs and makes sure they are healthy.
  (b) Jane loves to sing and she is thinking of joining a choir.
  (c) I liked the food at the bistro but I felt it was very expensive.
  (d) The children can walk to school or they can take the school bus.
  (e) Ben visits the local cinema often because it has the best popcorn in town.
  (f) The room was comfortable but it did not have a sea view.

59. Writing about the present and future

1 (a) We hope you can donate the refreshments for our festival.
  (b) I exercise regularly in the fresh air.
  (c) My friends at the gym encourage me to try harder.
  (d) Jim loves Estrick Bistro on the High Street.
  (e) Dogs bark loudly and frighten the children.

2 (a) Sam is very athletic; he runs in the park every day.
  (b) I eat at the bistro on special occasions.
  (c) When it is raining, we catch the bus to school.
  (d) Cars park on the pavement, making it dangerous to walk to school.
  (e) I hate it when dogs in the park bark near me.

3 (a) Ben is going to run in the park at the weekend.
  (b) I am going to volunteer in the animal shelter every day in the summer.

4 For example:
  I will celebrate at the bistro on my birthday.
  The children will need to find another route to school.

60. Writing about the past

1 (a) I applied to do work experience at the sports centre.
  (b) Ellie and I complained about the poor service in the bistro.
  (c) I filled in an application form to be a volunteer at the animal shelter.
  (d) The team worked hard to get the stock ready to sell.
  (e) My friend parked his car on the pavement.
  (f) The bistro lost money as it wasted a lot of food.

2 (a) John tried really hard to raise the money.
  (b) I was so scared on the rollercoaster, I cried.
  (c) We hurried to finish our meal as the bistro was closing.
  (d) The road is dangerous, so I carried my daughter to our front gate.

3 (a) John did a half marathon for charity.
  (b) We were late for the sponsored swim.
  (c) I had a lovely meal at the Bistro.
  (d) I saw a man jogging in the park.
  (e) Martin was so excited when he got a job at the animal shelter.
  (f) I ate at the college canteen regularly.
  (g) We took the long way to the shops.
  (h) It was late when I finally went to the supermarket.

61. Putting it into practice

Answers should include:
• detailed sentences
• correct use of verbs
• the same tense throughout.

62. Full stops and capital letters

1 At the end of a sentence

2 A capital letter

3 For proper names like John Smith
  For names of places like Birmingham
  For dates like Saturday 12 January 2016

4 (a) The Music Festival starts at 8pm. Mrs Jones and her daughter Janet will sing solos.
  (b) I had my wedding at Estrick Bistro. A jazz band plays there every Saturday night.

5 (a) I was so scared on the rollercoaster I had to shut my eyes!
  (b) I am not happy with the way you have handled my complaint about the room.
  (c) Why should dog owners take their dogs off the lead?
  (d) Do you want to try singing?

63. Commas and apostrophes

1

Commas	Apostrophes
Should not be used to separate two different ideas in a sentence.	Are used to show where letters are missing.
Can be used to separate items in a list.	Are used to show that something or someone belongs to someone or something.

2 Cars parked on the pavement will cause problems for children, people in wheelchairs and mothers with buggies.

  Instead of joining a gym you could try jogging, walking, swimming or using a fitness DVD at home.

3 (a) My friend's gym charges over £50 a month.
  (b) We are selling most of our shop's old stock.
  (c) Our local school is proud of its sports facilities.

4 (a) don't
  (b) I've
  (c) I'm

64. Putting it into practice

Answers should contain:
• one sentence ending with an exclamation mark
• one sentence ending with a question mark
• one sentence containing a list
• correct contractions and apostrophes if used.

107

65. Spelling

1 Believe/science/receive/deceive/receipt/friend

2 different/tomorrow/disappoint/possible/disappear

3 (a) safely
  (b) rudely when
  (c) which
  (d) extremely
  (e) Wednesday
  (f) lovely

66. Common spelling errors 1

1 (a) they're
  (b) to/two
  (c) where/our
  (d) too
  (e) you're/off
  (f) are/wear
  (g) our
  (h) their
  (i) your/there

2 (a) are
  (b) where
  (c) wear
  (d) There/to
  (e) you're

67. Common spelling errors 2

1 (a) The council should have taken action about the cars on the pavement.
  (b) You could have saved money by exercising in the park.
  (c) I bought a lot of expensive designer sports gear for going to the gym.
  (d) I know that the council takes this type of problem seriously.
  (e) I would have gone to another hotel if it hadn't been so late.

2 (a) My friend brought his family to Estrick Bistro for lunch.
  (b) A lot of injuries could have been prevented if the council had taken action.
  (c) I know you will want to help with the scanner appeal for the local hospital.
  (d) It wouldn't be right to make all dog owners keep their pets on a lead.
  (e) Something needs to be done now about the cars on the pavement.
  (f) Children would have a better idea about how to stay fit if they did more sport at school.

68. Common spelling errors 3

1 explanation   beautiful   persuade
  fierce   interrupt   straight
  although   business   preparation
  because   meanwhile   nervous
  decide   separate   autumn
  argument   unfortunately   actually
  experience   queue
  happened   remember

69. Plurals

1 (a) students/tests
  (b) churches
  (c) boxes
  (d) addresses
  (e) leaves
  (f) pluses

2 (a) flies
  (b) babies
  (c) cities
  (d) libraries
  (e) Sundays
  (f) families

3 (a) children
  (b) people
  (c) men
  (d) Women
  (e) feet

70. Checking your work

1 <u>Our</u> local cinema is the most amazing cinema <u>I've</u> ever been <u>to</u>. it has the biggest screen in <u>England</u>, a brilliant café, comfortable seats and the best popcorn <u>you've</u> ever tasted. <u>There</u> is a special <u>children's</u> show on <u>Sundays, which</u> is fun as they have games and competitions. I like it <u>because</u> they have enough staff so there are never any <u>queues</u>. Why <u>don't</u> you give it a go this weekend if <u>you're</u> stuck for something <u>to</u> do? <u>Believe</u> me, it is <u>definitely</u> worth a visit.

71. Putting it into practice

Answers should feature accurate spelling of commonly misspelled words and signs of checking/corrections.

72. Putting it into practice (example answer)

Answers should:
- use exciting sub-headings
- use some varied sentences
- use correct spelling
- have new detail in paragraph 3.

73. Putting it into practice (example answer)

Answers should:
- use all the information from the task bullet points
- have correct spelling, particularly of words from the task
- have detail added about price and reason for selling
- use complete sentences.

95. Practice paper: Reading

1 B

2 A

3 C

4 Visit the website, www.justmovealittle.com

5 Heading, columns, paragraphs image

6 Research suggests that short bursts of activity can prevent diabetes and high blood pressure.

  Short bursts of activity can improve the heart function of an adult over 45.

7 The app comes with instructions. It can be downloaded onto a phone, tablet or laptop.

8 B

9 D & E

10 A waterproof jacket and a bottle of water

11 There are plenty of stops along the way. The jog will be at a pace that suits everyone.

12 Simply turn up on Saturday morning

13 Exercise professionals will oversee a sensible workout session. You will be accompanied by experienced runners with first aid training.

99. Practice paper: Writing

Task 1

Estrick Council

Main Street

Estrick

ES1 3SW

18th August 2016

Your address

Dear Ms Suess,

I am writing to complain about the council's plans to cut the number of rubbish collections.

The rubbish bins on the beach are already overflowing, which is a big problem. The rubbish on the floor is a serious health hazard because people could trip over things and hurt themselves. Young families visit the beach and having rubbish over the floor means that it is not safe for children to play anymore. It is such a shame as people will stop coming to visit our lovely beach if nothing is done about this.

Please arrange for our beach to be cleaned up and don't cut the number of rubbish collections. I'm sure the locals would be happy to volunteer to help if you asked.

Regards,

Peggy Schumer

Task 2

To: d.jones@estricksports.net

Estrick Town Football Club sponsorship

Dear Danny,

I am emailing to ask you to sponsor Estrick Town Football Club so we can buy a kit. Our team needs the kit so that we can compete in the local league.

We can't afford a kit for the whole team so we're not able to compete. We would need £50 to buy the whole team a kit.

The youth football club encourages children to spend time outside and make friends, which is really important.

We're a community of 50 enthusiastic parents and children who would love the opportunity to compete in the local competition. We'd be very grateful if you could sponsor us.

Regards,

Omar Alshaker

Published by Pearson Education Limited, 80 Strand, London, WC2R 0RL.

www.pearsonschoolsandfecolleges.co.uk

Copies of official specifications for all Edexcel qualifications may be found on the website: www.edexcel.com

Text © Pearson Education Limited 2016
Edited by Jane Anson
Typeset by Jouve India Private Limited
Produced by Elektra Media
Original illustrations © Pearson Education Limited 2016
Illustrated by Elektra Media
Cover illustration by Miriam Sturdee

The right of Julie Hughes to be identified as author of this work has been asserted by her in accordance with the Copyright, Designs and Patents Act 1988.

First published 2016

19 18 17 16
10 9 8 7 6 5 4 3 2 1

British Library Cataloguing in Publication Data
A catalogue record for this book is available from the British Library

ISBN 978 1 292 14576 1

Printed in Italy by Lego S.p.A.

Acknowledgements
The author and publisher would like to thank the following individuals and organisations for permission to reproduce photographs:

(Key: b-bottom; c-centre; l-left; r-right; t-top)

Alamy Images: Dave Pattison 91/1, 91/2; **Corbis**: 84; **Shutterstock.com**: holbox 79/1, Jo Chambers 80, MeePoohyaPhoto 83, Microgen 79/3, Nikolay Dimitrov - ecobo 79/4, VectorLifestylepic 79/2

All other images © Pearson Education